LOVE IS LIKE THAT

Love is Like That

BY

CECIL ROBERTS

HODDER AND STOUGHTON

*The characters in this book are entirely imaginary
and bear no relation to any living person*

First printed .   .   .   1957

MADE AND PRINTED IN GREAT BRITAIN FOR
HODDER AND STOUGHTON LTD., LONDON, BY
HAZELL WATSON AND VINEY LTD., AYLESBURY AND LONDON

To

RUTH AND NORMAN BIRKETT

... Not that I support the rumour;
Let us watch it, you and I,
That we are not less than human,
Else, being caught, we may not cry
On the world to pity frailty.
Others judged them, never I!

from *A Ghost of Venice*

CONTENTS

CONTENTS

Book One

MERANO SYMPHONY

CHAPTER I

I

FROM his position in the pew at the side of the church he had a comprehensive view of the congregation. They were scattered as if to emphasise the emptiness of this beautiful building. It still retained its new look, having been built in Ligurio by a former large and wealthy English colony. It could hold eight hundred. At the moment it held twenty-four persons who represented half the present English colony in this Italian Riviera resort. Of these twenty-four persons most certainly half would be dead within ten years. They were quite cheerfully aware of the fact. Living in a community where most of them were approaching eighty, a funeral was a common event, taken in its stride along with bridge and cocktail parties. Those over the eighty-mark—there were fourteen of them in Ligurio, and eleven were present this morning—seemed the firmest-rooted against the gales of Time. They had forgotten how to die. Like one of those ingenious atmospheric clocks invented by the Swiss, they ran on, drawing their energy from the dust that fell on them.

The most dust seemed to fall on the most formidable representatives of the English colony, one Henry Crackenthorpe, aged ninety-two, and Mrs. Gavin, eighty-four. Mrs. Gavin easily outstripped her rival in irascibility. Her moods were quite unpredictable. She could be gracious, she could be bitter, and always she seemed preoccupied, something brooded deep within her. "I'll bet she gave old Gavin a hell of a time," said Crackenthorpe, an expert at giving people a bit of hell when in one of his moods. Happily these two members of the colony were outnumbered by the more even-tempered creatures. All in all, they were a kind, generous-minded body, laughing at each other's frailties.

The chaplain, the Reverend Tobias Smollett, now reading the lesson at the lectern, was a true Christian in spirit. A well-preserved eighty-one, memory apart, he was compact of mellowness and love towards his fellow men. The smile on his face was a blessing. The Reverend Tobias was in no way descended from the famous novelist, as he was quick to inform everyone. He had silver locks to match his silver voice, and the appearance of the elderly Wordsworth in benign repose. One felt he should have written *The Excursion*, but his genius expressed itself in a crewel needle. He was a peerless embroiderer. The *petit-point* that came from his hand was a work of art. His tall, fluffy-haired wife, straight from the brush of Gainsborough—she affected the white fichu at the neck that set off her beautiful skin—was equally skilled with plaster of Paris. Cherubs, swags of fruit, cameo portraits, classical panels, busts—the examples of her work cluttered up the drawing-room, the dining-room, the seven bedrooms, the study never studied in, and overflowed into the bathroom, the kitchen and the greenhouse. As one of these objects was always being knocked over, the Smolletts often emerged looking like a pair of millers. They moved and had their being in a cloud of white dust. The perfect wife, Amelia Smollett was artful. She contrived to rule her husband by a method of delicate retreat. It was a withdrawing action by which he found himself in complete agreement, and under the illusion that he had arrived at his position independently.

The chaplain, observed Aubrey Wellington from his corner pew, had become alarmingly absent-minded. One could not be too critical. Smollett was an honorary chaplain nobly struggling on. When he died there would be no one left to hold the services, and a chaplain would then have to be imported to bury the last of the flock. It seemed probable that this church would soon be closed for ever or be taken over for a concert hall, or even a night club, by the bursting

Italian community which had already engulfed the Tennis Club and the Social Hall. The solid British stone lion had been removed from the entrance of the latter.

The devaluation of the pound, meagrely dispensed by the Bank of England, critical of anyone desirous of living abroad instead of at Streatham or Purley, had dealt those institutions a deadly blow. Many of the English visitors, desperate for *lire* at the close of two or three weeks' sojourn, having become reckless in local shops, expected to be "assisted" by an "arrangement" with the permanent residents. They seemed unaware that owing to declining securities and devalued pounds many of the residents had been forced to give up villas, servants, gardeners, and were reduced to bed-sitting-rooms in cheap hotels. Too old and poor to go home, where they would be killed by the damp and fog, with no nest to go to and no one wanting them, they hung on, hoping there would be enough left to bury them. Money these days had shifted from the genteel to the brutal, from the artless to the artful. It was an age of high-powered cars conveying low-mannered people.

Often when death came the Reverend Tobias collected no burial fee. He gallantly went up the hill to the cypress-haunted cemetery, to a corner set apart for Protestants, and there pronounced the beautiful committal verses over the dead. They rested among earlier colonists, the English Mæcenases whose wealth in the Victorian and Edwardian eras had animated villas noisy with servants. Gone for ever, with their masters, were those smiling retainers, the Marios, Tonios, Marias and Lucias who all expected to inherit the villas they served in. Failing property, there would be good annuities, such as those left to Anna and Giorgio by the Misses Plummer.

All this world of affluence and graciousness had vanished. There was no paid chaplain in a large vicarage set in a sub-tropical garden, no ex-banker's widow who kept on the five gardeners out of kindness of heart. Aubrey Wellington, gazing at the sparse congregation, felt depressed. The death duties on the estates of these doomed survivors would not rate a hundred pounds a head.

The silver voice of the chaplain fluttered in the church. Something had surely gone wrong. There had been a desperate scrambling among the leaves of the Bible, a hunting for spectacles, a confused business with blue silk ribbon markers, and then, of all things, *The Song of Solomon*, which, as Smollett proceeded, caused increasing embarrassment to himself and the congregation. Having started with the wrong selection for the lesson, he felt bound to go on. For all of them gathered here any love song seemed inappropriate—all their love songs had been over long ago. Except for one. How singular, thought Wellington, that *The Song of Solomon* should be read this very morning! It was not possible—no, no one could know of his recent traffic with Eros.

He looked across the grey heads to the high window on the garden side. The sun flooded the vivid blue sky against which a black cypress threw its spear. He could just see the pink tulip magnolias in flower, the very banner of spring. The vision of them brought back a heady memory of youth, unfaded through almost forty years. Where now was Conchita, whose kisses he had stolen in the very shade of Chopin's ghost, on a March morning in the monastery garden at Valdemosa, high above the Majorcan plain? Conchita, Francine, Lucia, Meriel, Marietta, Sheila, all intoxicatingly lovable in their different ways and nationalities.

Many waters cannot quench love. . . . He imagined a long line of the women he had loved in his youthful wanderings. If after death, when he went to the place of assembly, they were all lined up confronting him! And those he could not remember . . . the thought made him smile. How they would stare at each other, how incongruous they would seem, Mexican, Italian, Rumanian, Scottish, Spanish. . . .

He looked across towards where Mrs. Gavin sat, a slim

figure in Quaker grey. It seemed impossible that romance had ever touched her, yet once she had been young and pretty, less censorious and forbidding. She was an unsociable member of the community. She lived alone, and seemed to belong to no one. Her second husband had been killed in the South African War. It seemed almost in the mists of antiquity, an insignificant event dwarfed by two World Wars. A widow for fifty years, fifty years of loneliness. Poor woman! How much could *The Song of Solomon* mean to her?

In the next pew sat Mrs. Callender, a gentle but equally reticent woman. The colony was hardly aware of her. She came to the English Library once a week, changed her books, and vanished. Behind her sat Colonel Slocombe, a noisy, bombastic old ass, a mountain of a man, lavishly generous when it came to subscribing for anything. He had just married his fourth wife, a pert little Frenchwoman much his junior, a widow with a good "dot". Wellington tried to imagine the nature of their romance. It was probably a quietly domestic workable affair. No, not quiet. Mrs. Slocombe had brought three French children with her. It was a noisy nest from all accounts.

His eyes travelled over the congregation. He noticed their frail bent figures and lined faces. Some were still beautiful in feature. Time had delicately etched its patterns on their faces; the filigree of frost had its own particular beauty. They had known ecstasy, they had suffered, they had been deprived, little by little, of possessions, of love, relations, friends. Their interests, if they had any beyond themselves, were now centred on the second and third generations that their creative episodes had provided.

A beautiful companionship still enriched a few of them. There was courtly old Commander Maysmith, the Beau Brummell of Ligurio, ninety, lean and tall as a Lombardy poplar, with his rakish brown felt hat (from Lock's), his shining brown shoes (bespoke), his bow tie (from Burlington Arcade), and gold-banded malacca cane. Grey eyes, ringed like an eagle's, were his gift from the sea. His delicate hands, with gold signet-ring carrying the crest of the Maysmiths of Langton Harcourt (the old manor decaying amid weeds and virginia creeper, with lead cupids and nymphs on stone pedestals, up to their thighs in ivy invading the terrace looking across the fields of the Ferney Hunt), were eloquent in movement when he talked. A Latin legacy, he explained, from a French great-grandmother whom a Maysmith had rescued from the guillotine during the French Revolution.

Beside the old Commander sat his wife, a colonel's daughter, who had run off in her eighteenth year with her father's French groom, a dark youth, sharp, shining and slim as the blade of a pocket-knife. This early scandal had resulted in a *cause célèbre* in France. To augment their meagre income the girl-wife had worked as an artist's model. The artist became so infatuated with the beautiful English girl that he persisted in pressing his attentions upon her. One night at a ball in Montmartre the artist became so amorous and offensive that the husband strangled him. A brilliant advocate procured his acquittal in the realm of the *crime passionnel*. The devoted young couple fled to Haiti to begin a new life. There in a revolution the groom was killed. A British destroyer put in to take off the Europeans. Thus Guy Maysmith first saw Maude Villemorin, a widow of twenty-four with an infant son of two. When the destroyer reached Trinidad, Lieutenant Maysmith, R.N., married the ravishing young widow with the lurid history.

Seated in the pew beside her husband, Mrs. Maysmith was still a lovely woman in her seventy-ninth year. Her French son was now a General with a distinguished career in the French Army, his half-brother, a Maysmith, was a famous surgeon. Wellington could see Mrs. Maysmith's aristocratic profile set against the stone pillar beyond the aisle, so calm, so venerable. Strange to recall the fire and passion that had consumed her youth! In the English colony they were exhibited as the perfect pair, well bred, courtly, lovely to behold and rewarding to know.

Aubrey Wellington reflected, as he looked at them, that, in his life, unlike Maude Maysmith's, the grand passion had caught him late, not early. Not a person present, for all their prying curiosity, their network of gossip, knew through what a fire he had passed in these recent days. A month ago all this had never happened to him. Miracles do not visit a man of sixty, but now he knew miracles did occur, that the heart was never quite dry, that ecstasy was not a monopoly of youth.

Many waters cannot quench love, neither can the floods drown it. How little Tobias Smollett realised the tremendous import of those words! Wellington knew now that not all the waters of the ocean could drown the love that had visited him so briefly, so overwhelmingly. And if they knew his story, how he would be condemned! What venom old Mrs. Gavin would visit on him, expressing censure and indignation. The dirty old man! The disgusting creature! Filthy! At his age! But, of course, there was always something . . . these geniuses. . . .

The implied insanity of genius always amused him. He was not a genius, but he accepted the term, having had it applied to him for so many years. The implication was that he could not be expected to behave as normal people behaved. Actually, he regarded himself as extremely sane, a balanced man, of regular habits, orthodox in mind and mindful of the conventions. No one ever took him for a composer. There was nothing Bohemian in his appearance. He dressed like an English gentleman. He was quiet in manner and speech. Through most of his life he had behaved decently, youthful follies apart, and throughout his life he had missed everything except success, which had become so habitual that he took it for granted. His compositions were played all over the world. He had conducted from the podiums of the capitals of Europe and of the American continent. For thirty years he had earned all the money he required. His wants being few, his tastes simple, his income always surpassed his outgoings, though he was quietly and consistently a generous man.

At sixty he was very much alone. He lived in a delightful villa above the town. It commanded a superb view of the Italian coastline, the semicircle of the sandy bay, the amphitheatre of the mountains, the blue sea closed in by two rocky promontories. His *ménage* was simple, an English secretary-housekeeper, an Italian butler and his cook-wife, a French parlourmaid, a Sicilian chauffeur and a gardener. Miss Porritt who ran his house had been with him for twenty years. She had nursed his second wife in her fatal illness, and had remained with him. She was good-humoured, fat, efficient, and, being able to satisfy her passion for poodles—she kept four—appeared to find all that she desired in life. If she had ever had a love affair, no scar was visible. A deep voice, and a solid way of putting down her large feet supplied sufficient grounds for Mrs. Gavin to assert that she was a Lesbian. Her adoration of an only niece, a lovely girl of eighteen, who came to spend her summer holidays at the villa, provided all the evidence Mrs. Gavin needed. "There are no men in her life, no," said Mrs. Gavin, "but have you seen her kiss that girl? Niece, indeed! Who says she's a niece?" Miss Porritt, fifty-seven, reticent, with only one man in her life, long dead in a military cemetery near Amiens, heard the Gavin version and smiled indulgently. She was one of many victims of the old dragon's tongue.

Wellington had not escaped. Mrs. Gavin suspected that he kept a mistress, an opera singer in Rome, which accounted for his frequent absences in that city. In truth he did keep an opera singer in Rome, but she no longer sang. She would never sing again. She was his pensioner. An old friend, associated with many of his early successes, she had poliomyelitis. He had taken her to see the best specialists in Europe, unavailingly. They had stayed at many hotels together in this heart-breaking quest. Some acquaintance of Mrs. Gavin's had reported that they occupied adjacent bedrooms at Sacher's, in Vienna. It was true. They always had adjacent bedrooms, for he often assisted her to rise and walk. Mr. Crackenthorpe had also a correspondent who reported that they breakfasted together, in dressing-gowns, on the bedroom loggia at the de luxe Hotel Stephanie in Baden-Baden. Again it was true, but the inference was untrue.

Mrs. Gavin and Mr. Crackenthorpe had occupied themselves very much with piecing together the details of his life. They had nothing else to do, and it was not difficult, for he lived, perforce, very much in the limelight. No detail missed them. "You were very late last night, a party? I saw the lights on in your villa at midnight," inquired Mr. Crackenthorpe. "Now you mustn't stay," said Mrs. Gavin, at a cocktail party. "Your dinner will be spoilt and Miss Porritt will be angry. You're having *scampi*, and they must be eaten hot and fresh!"

The great scandal in his life Mrs. Gavin did not know. No one knew. He almost regretted they did not know. It would stun them.

He looked out of the window. The noonday sun beat down on the magnolia blossoms and the scent of early pittosporum was in the air. Spring, after a cold winter, had descended on them with a rush. It passed so swiftly on this Italian Riviera, in such a riot of flowers, that it had vanished into the tourist-infested summer before one had realised its advent. Unlike in England, it was heralded by no bird voices, no reiterative cuckoo, no sweet-throated blackbird, no thrush pouring his song over the emerald grass. Here they shot all small birds. Sportsmen in heavy leggings, carrying clumsy guns, came home at the day's end with six tiny birds on a string as evidence of a day's sport.

The bird-song that had accompanied the lyric of Wellington's mountain idyll was still in his ears, for in the Tyrol they did not shoot small birds. One of these had sung its spring mating song, ravishingly joyous, on their balcony above the river as they made their last breakfast together.

> *O lyric Love, half-angel and half-bird*
> *And all a wonder and a wild desire!*

Browning's lines ran through his mind, an apt footnote to *The Song of Solomon* that Tobias Smollett was reading with considerable feeling.

He was making the best he could of it. It was one of those passages, with its emphasis on breasts and thighs and the raptures of the flesh, evaded by the Church. An old dog Solomon, but a wise old dog who knew a thing or two. Was it the spring in the air, coursing through the veins of the chaplain that had caused him to read it with such gusto? Wellington detected a surprised look on the faces of the congregation. Mr. Crackenthorpe, bent, had almost a leer. Mrs. Gavin, a grey monolith, sat stiffly upright, her mouth tight. Lady Crossley was smiling. She was one of those happy women who are always ready to smile, and to forgive. Only last month she had rendered Mrs. Gavin speechless with indignation at her lunch party. The English newspapers, and some of the Italian, had been filled with the unpleasant details of a trial in England. The prosecution, having failed in its first indictment, had dropped the second, and gone muckraking into the past. It had secured a conviction by suborning two wretched youths to turn King's evidence. An Italian at the table, the case having been mentioned, had asked why the British Press gloated over such insalubrious details. "The Dorian vice would not raise a comment on the Continent. We know these things occur but we do not publicise them. We are satisfied with the Code Napoléon."

"In England we have a code of morals. On the Continent we know there is no such thing," said Mrs. Gavin, bitingly.

Lady Crossley gave her sweet smile. "In England, as else-where, we have husbands who beat their wives and seduce their typists. We have a Society for the Prevention of Cruelty to Children. It seems very necessary. Here there is no such society. It isn't necessary. As for this unpleasant *auto-da-fé* of unhappy homosexuals, surely there is enough rape, murder, and robbery with violence to keep the police occupied?"

There was a chorus of assent which Mrs. Gavin met with an icy stare. She would have left the table, but the table was too good after the dreary fare she subsisted on in the Hotel Mondovi. And this from an ex-Governor's wife! The world had fallen to pieces.

II

The service drew to its close. "Hymn one hundred and ninety-seven," said Tobias Smollett, *The King of Love my Shepherd is*. Mrs. Smollett's fingers went down on the organ keys. They began to sing, with wavering voices.

Hugh Trent picked up his stick from the floor in readiness for going forth, gallantly lame, with the collection plate. He was eighty-one and took an hour to walk a mile. He got here, every Sunday morning. He enjoyed singing the hymns. At Westminster he had been a solo boy in the Abbey choir, with a scholarship, and Queen Victoria had once commanded him to sing at Windsor Castle. Every Thursday he made a painful journey to the church, to select the hymns, to try them on the organ, while he loosened up his voice. "Not as fluty as I was," he observed with a wry smile.

Wellington reached down for the five-hundred-lire note in his pocket. Five hundred lire, that was the tip he had given the hotel porter at Merano on the morning he had said goodbye to Anne. He still owed her five hundred lire, for after settling the bill and leaving, he had only a five-thousand note, and had borrowed from her for the taxi fare.

He had been home three days, and away fourteen. Two of the colony had died while he was away. Philip Farlow had vanished, a gentle soul, and at seventy-two rather young to leave this circle. But life had lost its lure for him when his

wife had died a year earlier. His daughter Jill, playing in
New York, had thrown up her part in a Broadway success
and had flown over to comfort him. She tried to persuade
him to go back with her, but he had refused. "I should be
quite lost there," he told Wellington. "In fact I'm lost anywhere now," he added, with a sad smile. He had played
bridge at the club until the day he died. Three days later,
Paula Plowright, with dyed red hair, a cigarette always in
her mouth and the whisky bottle always at hand, good-
hearted, outspoken, spendthrift, had been found dead in bed
at the Hotel Bellavista where she lived in one room surrounded by photographs of a son, two daughters and seven
grandchildren. She was jokingly called "The Ginger Peril"
and rejoiced in the nickname.

And while Philip Farlow and Paula Plowright were dying
he was living in a delirium of love. It didn't make sense. It
didn't make sense to draw out of the lottery of life, towards
its end, such a prize. Happily life began with hope and
illusion. His own start had been auspicious. He had survived
a horrible long war. He had married a lovely girl, was
ecstatically happy, at twenty-four a boy captain, with a baby
son. Then he was badly wounded at Vimy Ridge and in
hospital for two months. The tiny flat they had taken was
let. His wife had gone to live with her mother in Bedford.
He had a month's leave with his wife and son in a house lent
to them in Chelsea, but it was a harrowing experience.
Something had happened to Sheila. Young, physically
starved through months of absence and suffering, he came
home, eager, amorous. She met his advances coldly. She
would give no reason. One evening he went home, with the
summons to rejoin his regiment in France in his pocket. He
wondered how he would break the news, how she would take
it. He paused outside the white door with the Adam knocker,
steeling himself for the ordeal. In the narrow hall he found
an envelope on the table addressed to him in Sheila's handwriting. He opened it, and his paradise lay shattered.

"I am very sorry, Aubrey, but I cannot deceive you any longer. I am desperately in love with someone else. I shall never trouble you again; you were always kind. Be kind still and leave me alone. I have sent Alan down to your mother. He is yours, of course.

SHEILA."

Just that, and a silent house. She had turned down the bed, put out his pyjamas, and placed the milk in the larder. She had left two dresses in the wardrobe, and her toothbrush in the bathroom. Every other trace of her had vanished. He went out and walked about Chelsea, all night, crying like a child. In the morning he wired his mother: *Look after Alan. Close down the house. Writing.* Having written a letter of instruction to his mother, sleepless, he walked to Victoria Station, saw the R.T.O. and in an hour got a passage back to France. He tried desperately to get killed. Ironically his recklessness gained him an M.C. One morning, coming out of the trenches, he received some mail. There was a letter from Sheila's bullet-headed brother, a major in the Irish Guards. "Desperately sorry, old man. I hear my sister's fallen for a Yank. Hope he'll take her to Harlem and beat hell out of her."

He beat hell out of her. Three years later she divorced him, married again, deserted her husband, came home, tried to claim the boy, and then suddenly was stricken with consumption. She sent for him. He went down to Midhurst Sanatorium and could hardly recognise the wraith he saw. They cried together. She asked him to forgive her and to bring Alan to see her. He forgave her and promised. Before he could get Alan down from his mother's home she was dead. She was thirty.

By this time he was on his way to fame as a composer, with two symphonies performed and published. Four years later he married again. He did not delude himself. He was not deeply in love. His conception of love, after such brutal usage, had changed, but Alan needed a mother and he needed a home. The girl he married had a passion for music, she was pretty, eager and affectionate. He felt he was lucky until something emerged. She had a streak of religious mania. She would not bring children into such a sinful world. His music should emphasise the spiritual values of life. She had such a clear consciousness of God that she knew exactly what His will was in any difficulty. It always co-incided with her own. God was her junior partner in the direction of events. She was a flawless housekeeper. "God keeps the house," she said to a friend who congratulated her. Suddenly Alan was stricken with spinal meningitis and died in twenty hours in the school hospital, aged fourteen. She had been a wonderful foster-mother. "We loved him too much, too selfishly. God has chastened us, and taken dear Alan to His bosom," she said. "Don't talk damned rot!" he said to her, desperate. "Aubrey, don't blaspheme! God's will must be our will," she replied softly.

She grew worse after that. She refused him her bed. "We must purge ourselves of carnal desires," she said. A Canadian revivalist came over and worked congregations into religious hysteria, manipulating the herd instinct with a Hitlerian technique of mass formations, spotlights and choral singing. Freda was at home less and less. She joined the revivalist troupe and went to Leeds, Liverpool, Oxford, Birmingham, Glasgow and Edinburgh, in the wake of the missioner. Finally she proposed crossing the Atlantic with him. "There are deeper spiritual currents emanating from the New World (she called it The Noo World, after her leader), I want to study them." She had plenty of money in her own right, her late father had made a fortune in plastics and left the family wealthy. Freda bought a twelve-hundred-pound mink coat to protect her from the New York winter, and set off ecstatic-ally to study God's deeper currents.

Wellington was missing his wife less and less since Alan's death. His engagements took him across the Continent. He conducted in Vienna, Rome, Paris, Berlin and Amsterdam. Miss Porritt, the tranquil, the infallible, took charge of the household. When Freda returned she hardly noticed her, so busy was she with her committees. The early enthusiasm for mass conversion had badly slumped, the surge of sinners seemed to have gone back to the worship of film stars and royalties. Freda after her immersion in the deeper spiritual currents of the New World was oblivious of this.

In her fortieth year her dynamic energy failed her. Letters no longer poured from her pen. With failing health she began to lose her certainty, she fell into mental doubt and distress. He came nearer to her then than at any time in their fifteen years of marriage. Her last words were the most pathetic. "Aubrey, I have neglected you. God has chastened me for presumption. Forgive me." She died gently in his arms. His second marriage had given him nothing, had been a failure.

Throughout all these years he had been faithful to her. It was not from lack of opportunity. In the world of music human emotions are turbulent. He was pursued by women, clever, rich, beautiful, crazy, the glamour of fame added to the potency of music. They mobbed him at the door of the artistes' room, thronged round the limousine waiting at the stage door. They hung about the lobby of his hotel, auto-graph hunting. Suave, tall, good-looking and well groomed, taking pleasure in the company of pretty women, he had plenty of temptation. But the shock of his first marriage had done something to him. Freda could have warmed him back to life, but he felt no fire within her. Neither her mind nor her body was ever his. His work became his passion. For the last fifteen years he had lived quite alone. The pleasure had gone out of a fulfilled career. He became indifferent to his fame. Life came back to him only when he stood on the podium and raised the baton. He had composed little for five years, but his fame on the Continent ran like a gathering wave. His opera *Orestes* was in constant production.

He had many friends but no intimates. An only son of an

only son, he had no circle of relations, for better or worse.
He was impulsive, warm-hearted. He loved children and
would have been a deeply affectionate father. Fate had
robbed him of all this. Four years ago, motoring through
Ligurio on his way to conduct at the Florence Musical
Festival, he had seen a villa for sale. Its position was superb,
above terraced gardens ablaze with flowers. It was a porti-
coed villa, wide-windowed, commanding magnificent views
of a crescent bay of golden sand locked in by headlands of the
Ligurian mountains. The villa was not large, nine rooms.
It was completely furnished, the late owner, a retired Indian
civil servant, having died. The nephew inheriting it did not
want it. The price was modest. The furniture included a
Steinway grand piano and a small music library. It had
other assets which could not appear in a bill of sale. These
were a gardener and his wife living in the lodge, a pair of
warm, smiling Italians. They had a small son, a sprite of ten,
chubby, with colt-like brown legs, brilliant black eyes and
a mop of sun-smitten chestnut locks. On Wellington's first
visit he hid in the dappled shadows of the vine pergola. On
the second visit, attracted like a wasp to a jampot, he fluttered around the Jaguar car in the drive.

"Is that your boy?" asked Wellington.

"*Si, signore*. Adelio, come and say *Buono giorno* to the
signore," called his father.

The boy came forward, hesitantly, bronzed, graceful as a
gazelle. He offered a thin hand and appraised the stranger
seriously. Later he became a faithful shadow.

Miss Porritt was in ecstasy. She spent hours quoting Byron,
Shelley, Keats and Browning. Her Italian was not as good
as her French and German, but it sufficed. And there was
young life in the house. On the day he signed the contract he
called at the villa, and informed the gardener and his wife
that their jobs were secure. Young Adelio rushed to him
in wild delight. Wellington lifted him up, laughing. The
boy's arms went round his neck. He held him, soft, affec-

tionate, for a moment, then he lowered the lithe young body between his hands, suddenly shaken by a memory. Alan's ghost came back.

There were four halcyon years, with coming and going of guests. He gave Adelio piano lessons. The boy was a born musician, precociously intelligent. Fearing he would be spoilt by too much adoration from parents and relations, not to mention himself and Miss Porritt, he came to an agreement with the gardener and sent him to a school in Lausanne. "He will never be our Adelio again, *signore*. He will come back a young gentleman, but we must not stand in his way."

"If he has half of your good manners and a quarter of his mother's good sense he will know he has wonderful parents, Francesco."

"*Tante grazie, signore.*"

Wellington returned after his tours to the Villa Tiberio. He was slowing up. Ambition no longer spurred him. He read in the shade of the pergola, dozed there after lunch, listened to the sounds of the Italian mountainside, the braying of a donkey, the timeless jingle of the campanile bells below him, the hooting of steamer sirens out in the bay, the purr of distant traffic on the Via Aurelia below, or the sudden burst of an opera aria from a workman at an adjacent villa. And always there was the warmth, the blue radiance of the sky, the vine-leaf shadows in the moonlight under the pergola, the brilliant stars above the sentinel cypresses.

He was now approaching sixty. Where had those twenty years between forty and sixty gone? Work, fulfilment of ambition and a war had imperceptibly swallowed them up. He began to wake too early. He paid too much attention to *The Times* obituary column. Colleagues vanished from the scene. One day he scrapped his address book and began a new one, unable to bear the scored-out names. He noticed that Miss Porritt was slower about the house. Like her, he, too, was slowing up. Yet he felt young at heart still, and this mental youthfulness induced an unnamed unrest. His youth and young manhood had been cheated of something. He avoided naming the thing that had eluded him. It was something that, at sixty, should be behind him. He had been robbed of physical ecstasy. Sex.

He hated the word. He hated the vulgar parade of it in the popular Press, the blatant worship of it in the cinema with its sickening parade of nude girls with Hottentot breasts and undulant bellies. Hollywood had found the mainspring of all life and commercialised it. It shamelessly exploited the biological fact that the whole force of creation was centred in the irrepressible impulse of the race to perpetuate itself. Not all the religion and philosophy in the world could avail against this basic truth. This was the dynamo that drove the world, that moved nations, that created and destroyed civilisations. It might be sublimated and assume the lyrical quality of love, but the tiger in the house was never quite domesticated. It was easy for age with its slaked thirst and burnt-out fires to counsel the young. Philosophy grew when passion died. To have missed the wild heady moment was to have missed the peak of life. The cruel truth bore down upon him when he saw the young in each other's arms. The intensity of his loss was emphasised by his own experience. One woman he had failed to hold, one to kindle. In the barren desert of his middle age he had come to persuade himself there had been no loss. A puritan complex had built a protective wall around his inner nature, shutting out reality. Suddenly, on a day in March, there had been a Jericho crash. The trumpet had sounded and the lonely citadel of his heart had fallen.

The violence of it still perturbed him. Contrary to all his philosophy and self-respect, the manner of his fall had become a triumph, an exalted memory. "You are a dirty old man, driven by your gross sensual appetite," proclaimed the voices of a dozen Mrs. Gavins within him. "It was an unbelievably beautiful moment; never to be repeated in your life, never to be forgotten," proclaimed a louder voice within him. *The Song of Solomon* echoed that voice. *Many waters cannot quench love, neither can the floods drown it.* Neither could age wither it.

III

When at last they came out of the church into the warm noonday, little Mrs. Viviani, the English wife of an Italian Lothario who had deserted her, accosted Wellington.

"You were deep in a daydream all through the service, Sir Aubrey. What was it—a new composition, or merely boredom?"

"Neither."

"And you won't tell me?"

"I would not tell anyone," he answered.

"You couldn't be more provoking!" she cried.

"You should have concentrated on the service, not on me," he said.

"The service! Dear old Tobias was very funny with that *Love Song*. Come and join us for a drink at Valentino's. Hugh and Sir John and Meriel are coming. We want to hear all about your trip to Munich."

He excused himself, saying something about an accumulation of letters at the villa, and went off alone.

Smollett's choice for the lesson had perturbed him. It seemed almost intuitive. And what an odd thing for the old boy to read to a community like this! One other thing had slightly perturbed him on setting forth to church. Miss Porritt came out on to the terrace with a book in her hand and settled on the swing lounge.

"Have you ever read *Indian Summer of a Forsyte*?" she asked, holding up a book.

"No. By whom?"

"Galsworthy, one of his stories I missed somehow. It's about an old man who fell in love with a young girl—quite decently, of course. It's really charming. I've almost finished it. He makes it quite credible."

"It must have taken a lot of doing," he said defensively.

He hurried off the terrace. And within the same hour *The Song of Solomon* from old Smollett! It wasn't possible that anyone in Ligurio could know what had happened to him this last week in Merano. And now Mary Viviani with her sharp eyes had detected him in a daydream.

He walked slowly back to the villa. There was an hour before his guests, a musical couple from England, and the chaplain and his wife came to lunch. He sat down in his favourite chair under the pergola, and lit a cigar. He was still, only forty-eight hours off the train, shaken by his experience. He looked at his watch. It was just after noon. In seven hours, Anne would be joining the Paris night express from Munich, en route to Cherbourg, out of Europe, out of his life to the New World that had produced her.

A daydream, indeed. He lived it all over again as he sat back and smoked his cigar.

CHAPTER II

I

HE had gone to Munich at the beginning of March to conduct a production of Mozart's *Die Entführung aus dem Serail* and to give a lecture at the university. His visit had been a great success, both the opera house and the auditorium had been packed. He had been much fêted and entertained. Munich was rising from the ashes of the Nazi era, a wave of prosperity was sweeping over the scarred city. He had known it well in his youth, a city of excellent musical productions, and the scene of the early Strauss's triumphs. His old friend, Professor Herman Salzer, asked him whether on his last evening he would allow him to invite a few of his students to meet him. The genial old boy took them all out to a vast *Bierkeller* on the outskirts of the city. About twenty students had been invited, and they passed a jovial argumentative evening. The boys and girls were somewhat shy at first, but their awe of him soon vanished. They talked eagerly in a mixture of German and English. Five of the students were American.

Very late, too late, for he was leaving for Italy at eight o'clock the next morning, the party broke up. The Professor motored him back to the Hauptbahnhof Hotel, where he was staying. Seven persons crammed themselves into the limousine, three youths, two girls, the Professor and himself. On the far side of the Professor sat one of the girls. In the darkness of the car her profile was hardly visible. She did not join in the conversation, but she had smiled at him when inadvertently his hand, placed along the ledge behind the Professor, to give space in the crowded back seat, had touched her bare neck. On arrival at the station they all got out to bid him good night and *Aufwiedersehen*. One of the girls

L.T.—2

could not have known he was leaving Munich so soon, for on shaking his hand she said, "It's been such a wonderful evening, Sir Aubrey. I hope we shall meet again soon."

"Alas, I leave at eight o'clock in the morning," he replied.

"Oh, that is too bad!"

He had not noticed before, that, from an intonation in her voice, she was an American.

After a solemn handshaking, and much bowing from the young students, he left them and entered the hotel.

His room, overlooking the street, was noisy, and it was one o'clock before he fell asleep. He was sleeping when the room telephone called him at half-past six, as arranged. He was a man who always arrived at a station early. At half-past seven he had breakfasted, packed, and was closing his portmanteau when the telephone rang. He was surprised to be called by anyone at this early hour. He picked up the receiver.

"Yes?" he asked.

"Sir Aubrey?"

"Yes."

"Probably you won't recall me, I'm Anne Beveridge."

"Yes?" he said vaguely.

"I was one of the Professor's party last night."

"Oh, yes."

"I thought I would like to come and see you off," said the voice.

"That is very kind of you, but I am leaving in a few minutes."

"Yes, I know. At eight o'clock. I am downstairs in the hotel lobby."

"Oh!" he said, and then after a pause added—"I am coming down now."

He put down the receiver. He was a little annoyed. Doubtless one of those gushing girls with musical ambitions, who hung about hotel lobbies and artistes' rooms, autograph book in hand. But this pestering rarely began in the early morning. She had been one of the members of the party, so he must be polite to her. None of the girls had talked much. Two of the boys, deeply earnest young Germans, had cross-examined him deferentially. One spoke excellent English, so took the lead. His own German was not really adequate.

When he came down into the empty hotel lobby a young woman rose from a chair and came towards him somewhat shyly. It was the girl of the previous evening who had sat on the other side of the Professor in the car.

"Miss Beveridge?" he asked, holding out his hand.

"Yes, Sir Aubrey. I hope you don't mind. I always dislike leaving a strange city alone, so I thought I would give myself the pleasure of seeing you off."

"That is very kind of you," he replied.

There was an awkward pause. She had no autograph book. He glanced at the clock. It was half-past seven, early for an interview.

"Can I walk with you to the train?" she asked. This time she smiled at him. Without observing her too closely he saw she was fair, pretty, young. Possibly twenty-two or so. Her voice was pleasant.

"Certainly—shall we go?" he answered. He gave his bag to the porter. "Will you take it to the train—the Milan eight-o'clock express," he said.

The porter took the bag. The revolving hotel door opened on to a corridor of shops that led to a vestibule in front of the platform gates. It was a new station. As they passed a café he had an idea. He had no relish for those inane conversations with which people fill in time until the train departs.

"Shall we have a cup of coffee?" he asked his companion.

"Oh, thank you, that would be nice."

They entered. A man was swabbing the floor, but they found a dry corner, with a table. He ordered coffee. He could observe her fully now. She was of medium height, slim, with a mass of flaxen hair, combed down from the crown of her head. A front fringe was clipped straight across her broad forehead. At the back of her head the hair hung wavily over the nape of her neck. She wore a simple pale blue frock, wide open at the neck, almost a Tyrolean *dirndl* in pattern, with very short sleeves, frilled and gathered in at the shoulders. She wore no stockings, and had white shallow low shoes that contrasted with the brown tan of her legs. The feet and ankles were pretty and neat. Her legs were sturdy but shapely. Her hands were beautiful. The most notable feature was her eyes. They were a limpid blue, the blue of a mountain stream lit by sunlight. She was a Scandinavian type, fresh complexioned, as though she had lived in the wind all her life and had been sweetened by it. There was a curious blend of diffidence and frankness in her speech. His Scandinavian surmise was not wrong. Her mother was Swedish, her father American of Scotch descent. She was born in Santa Monica, California.

"And how did you come to be here in Munich?" he asked.

"I got a Fulbright Scholarship at the University of California."

"You are very young?"

"Not so very—twenty-four. That's getting old."

They laughed together at that.

"Then how do you regard sixty?"

"Some people are never sixty. Their souls keep them young. You're really very young, aren't you, Sir Aubrey? I watched you conducting last Tuesday night. You might have been twenty, except that no one of twenty, or forty even, could have conducted that Mozart opera so knowledgeably."

"Thank you, Miss Beveridge."

"Oh, Anne, please. I'm Anne to everybody."

"How long have you been over here?"

"Two years."

"Studying music—do you play?"

"Very little. I'm in Professor Salzer's class—counterpoint and orchestration."

"Then a very serious musician!"

"Yes—but I haven't really got it, you know, not born. You must have it that way—like Stravinski or Carlo-Menotti. If you squeeze them they exude music."

"Have you tried squeezing them?" he asked playfully.

Her voice rippled in laughter.

"No—but you know what I mean! You couldn't squeeze anything out of the Professor! I'm not criticising. He's a wonderful teacher, but it's theory, all theory, out of the brain."

"I don't disagree with that. How long do you remain here?"

"I'm leaving for home next month—I sail from Cherbourg in three weeks. I've had a wonderful two years, one year in Vienna, one in Munich. I'll have my doctor's degree and then teach—somewhere."

"Somewhere? Not at home?" he asked.

"I've no home really. Both my parents are dead. My only brother's with the Army in Japan. We were brought up by an aunt in Laramie, Wyoming. There's nothing for me there."

She spoke without any reservations, a child of the new world, self-reliant and experienced. Her smile was entrancing, as also the manner in which she shook back her flaxen hair. A patch of it was sun-bleached.

He paid the bill and they left the café. The hall porter was at the ticket gate with the portmanteau. He followed them in and placed it in a first-class compartment. Tipped, he bowed and left them. They stood and talked on the platform. He was still puzzled though pleased by her presence. He learned that she lived on the other side of Munich and had risen at six.

"Do you usually rise at six?" he asked.

"Never!" she said, with her silvery laugh and a shake of her flaxen hair.

The moment of departure arrived. The guard was hurrying the passengers into the coach. He was about to shake her hand when, as if on impulse, she put a folded paper in his.

"That's my address," she said quickly, with a nervous air.

"Oh—oh, thank you," he said, with undisguised surprise. "It was very kind of you to take all this trouble—I wish we had met sooner. Good-bye, and thank you again." He took her hand in his, and held it briefly.

She made no reply as their hands parted, but she looked at him with her candid eyes. Suddenly she leaned forward, kissed him on the cheek, turned and walked quickly away.

Startled, he watched her, motionless for a moment or two, and then entered the coach. The train was moving when he reached his compartment. He looked out of the window. She had vanished. He sank back on the soft cushions. A strange sensation ran through him. He sat back in the empty compartment and closed his eyes. The train threaded a labyrinth of sheds, the weak morning sunshine fell on the dark litter of sidings. The warmth of her firm kiss was still on his cheek, the spring freshness of her about him. An infatuated schoolgirl, his mind said. But that would not do. She was a young woman of twenty-four, qualifying for a doctor's degree in music. She had the easy, uninhibited confidence of a child of the New World. Hero-worship? He had suffered from it a great deal, and knew all the phases of this derangement, particularly the American form. "Bobby-soxers" they called them, the girls who mobbed crooners and film stars, hid under their beds, and lay down in front of their cars. But he was no crooner with raven locks and a sob-laden voice. Nor was she a bobby-soxer. She expressed poise, sanity and self-respect.

Why had this girl risen at six o'clock and crossed Munich to accompany him to his train? He was a man of sixty, "well-preserved" as the menacing phrase expressed it, with no Casanova temperament encouraging advances.

He remembered the slip of paper he had put in his waist-coat pocket. He took it out. It was not a visiting-card, but a bit of paper torn out of a score book with staff lines across it. On it, in a very legible firm hand she had written: *Anne*

Beveridge. Tegernseelandstrasse 64b. Munchen. 9. The address surprised him. She was leaving soon and sailing for America.

Well, odd as it all was, it was a very pleasing episode. Elderly men were not seen off at the station early in the morning by charming girls whom they scarcely knew. He would remember this Munich visit. When he wrote to thank the Professor for his hospitality he would ask him about his pupil Anne Beveridge. No, he wouldn't. It would not be fair to the girl. But he would always wonder about her, why she came, why she kissed him. It couldn't be mere infatuation, not at his age. His fame? It scarcely warranted such attention. A mixture of both, or just youthful enthusiasm and impulsiveness?

He opened a marked newspaper that had been sent to his hotel. It had a long critique of his conducting of *Die Entführung aus dem Serail*. He began to read it, but the words failed to possess his senses. He had been kissed on the platform by a lovely girl. It deranged him a little, and left him beating about for an explanation. He sat back, closed his eyes while the train shook off the suburbs of Munich. It was Wednesday, the fourteenth of March. Next Monday it was his sixtieth birthday. It would be warm and sunny in Ligurio. Here it was still cold and rainy. He was not going through to Ligurio. The train arrived too late. He had planned to stay a couple of nights in Bolzano. He liked the Hotel Greif and had booked a room. He would arrive before noon. On the morrow he would go over to nearby Merano for the day. He had never seen it and had heard much of its attraction.

He picked up the marked critique and read it. It was acute, complimentary to him and the orchestra. He had taken the second act a little too fast. He agreed, but both singers and orchestra had been caught up by its Mozartian gaiety and he had not checked them. It was an early vintage. One sentence of the critique had a word two inches long. It was beyond him, but from the context he gathered the sense.

When a waiter came he ordered coffee and biscuits. At

Innsbruck three travellers entered his compartment. One was a very fat nun, a Blue Sister, and her nursing order turned his mind to old Crackenthorpe and his runaway marriage with a Blue Sister which had had a comic retribution. The nun settled herself. She was so fat that she pushed up one of the arms to give herself more space. She closed her eyes and slumbered.

The train was prompt in Bolzano. A pleasant room awaited him. After lunch he dozed, took a walk along the river bank, dined in the garden of the hotel, wrote a few letters and went to bed. He tried hard to dismiss the episode on the platform that morning, but it kept obtruding. A vision of her fresh loveliness began to obsess him. Nothing so unconventional, so surprising, had happened to him for years. A lovely ingenuous girl had crossed Munich to see him off, had talked with him vivaciously, had kissed him, and fled. He began to regret deeply that he would never see her again.

II

The next morning it was clear and sunny, with a warmth in the air. He took a train to Merano, and in about half an hour arrived. He was delighted with the little town from the moment that he emerged from the station and walked down the tree-lined avenues. There were gay fruit-stalls by the old castle. The ancient arcaded streets, the fourteenth-century Gothic church with its tall spire, the embankment, green with poplars that lined the swift slaty river, the bridges spanning it, the Kurhaus and the elaborate garden beds, ablaze with flowers, the little bandstand, the cafés spread over the pavement, all evoked an air of the nineteenth-century gaiety when Merano had been a rendezvous of fashionable Austrians. It was still, despite its transfer to the Italian flag after 1918, a German-speaking town of the Tyrol. The boys wore *lederhosen*, and although most of the notices were written in Italian he found that the shopkeepers talked

German, and responded reluctantly when he spoke the
imposed language, and readily when he spoke German.
Something of a backwater, it had not, like Bolzano, adapted
itself to a new age and a new nationality. He noticed that
Strauss and Lehar predominated in the programme of the
Kurhaus orchestra that played in the open bandstand each
afternoon. He discovered a short cable railway that led to
a promenade built along a terrace on the mountain side. He
ascended and was enchanted by the winding floral walk, the
distant vista of the snow-covered mountains, the panorama
of the valley with the old town, its steeple and ancient roofs
clustering along the course of the river. At every bend of the
promenade there was a fresh vista of the majestic Alps,
brilliant in the noonday sun.

Presently he came upon a typical Tyrolean chalet, its
wooden balcony ablaze with pots of geraniums and petunias.
The windows under the deep overhanging roof commanded
a view of the whole valley. Above the entrance was a board
on which had been nailed a notice. *Zimmer zu vermieten.*
Room to let. What a perfect spot for a honeymoon! It was the
epitome of romance. A line of Tennyson came into his head—

Come down, O maid, from yonder mountain height . . .

He walked on by the chalet. Had he been forty years
younger, had a lovely, eager girl kissed him impulsively . . .

He stopped, a little dizzy with his fanciful embroidery.
A girl had kissed him impulsively. He did not feel old—she
could not have thought him old. Perhaps here, in this enchanted scene, in this keen mountain air, the whole world
at the Spring below him . . .

Zimmer zu vermieten.

He turned back and entered under the garden archway.
There was no harm in enquiring, in playing with an Arca-
dian fancy. He mounted the flagged steps and came to an
open doorway. The little hall was furnished with home-
carved furniture, an old cuckoo clock, some antique guns

and antlers on the walls. He found a bell that tinkled. A dog barked. There was silence. He was about to ring again when he heard footsteps. A stout elderly man with side-whiskers emerged from a passage. He had a jovial, well-nourished face.

"I see you have rooms to let?"

"*Ja, mein Herr*. Please come in. I will show you the house."

He led him up a wide creaking staircase. On the landing he opened a door into a large bedroom. Another door off it gave access to a balcony with flower-pots and a magnificent view. The bed was a large double one, wooden. There was a table with a gay floral cloth, a heavy wardrobe, a wash-basin with hot and cold water taps.

"We have another room with balcony, and two single beds," said the portly landlord.

He opened a communicating door. The second room was even more delightful.

"What is the rate for this room?"

"With pension for two, four thousand lire a day," said the smiling landlord. "Baths included."

It was modest enough.

"The room is vacant for this week-end?"

He seemed to hear his voice apart from himself, the question was so much against his own prudence.

"Alas—no. I thought you were enquiring for the season. We have an American gentleman arrives tomorrow. He comes every year at this time, from Baltimore, with his wife and sister. They take the whole floor for a month. This is their fourth year. They love the place. Mr. and Mrs. Blumenthal. They are very democratic. He has the largest factory for——"

"Oh, yes—then it is useless," said Wellington, cutting the landlord short. He was immensely relieved that the room was not to let. His folly had been frustrated. "Good morning and thank you," he said, turning to leave.

"*Aufwiedersehen, mein Herr*. Some other time, I hope."

He walked rapidly down the flagged path to the gate. He

was perspiring. What had possessed him to contemplate such folly!

He went back into the town. He had no appetite for lunch, and seeing a sign *Milch Bar* under the stone arcades of a narrow street, he went in. It had two tables and chairs. It was also a general store with yoghourt, cheeses, sausages, biscuits. A rosy little man greeted him from behind the counter. He bought a bottle of milk and a packet of biscuits, and went to one of the tables. Presently a dapper middle-aged man came in, ordered a glass of milk, and sat down at the adjoining table. He bowed as he sat down, and presently addressed him.

"You are a visitor, sir? Your first time in Meran?"

He spoke excellent English. Since he said Meran and not Merano he was obviously Austrian, like most of the population. He began to talk of the place.

"Ah, you should have seen it, sir, in the old days! The first war shook it. The second war killed it. We had soldiers in all the hotels. You know what soldiers are in any place! They wrecked the Stephanie. It was a de-luxe hotel. All the fashion of Austria came there—and latterly we were getting the Italian nobility. It has not reopened. I was the concierge for fifteen years. So I am out of work. Happily, I have a little stationer's shop. If you require anything, sir, here is my card."

He continued to talk affably but with a certain dignified reticence. As a youth he had had his training at Marienbad.

"I often saw your King Edward VII. He was a great gentleman. Always a long cigar, a little fox-terrier and two or three pretty ladies."

"Not quite the Venetian formula—'a little mass in the morning, a little gamble in the afternoon, a little lady in the evening'?" asked Wellington.

"I should say, sir, from what I saw, that if you cut out the mass, the formula held good!" said the ex-concierge, laughing.

"Do you know of a nice quiet hotel here?" asked Wellington.

Again, was this his own voice asking the question, prompted by the romantic chalet on the mountainside? The idea had lodged itself though it was utterly preposterous.

"All the hotels are quiet, sir. It is out of season. But if you require a discreet hotel, a friend of mine has just opened one. It has a splendid position on the river bank, and has a most excellent cuisine. The Alexandra. I most strongly recommend it. But I must add, there is no lift."

Discreet. Why had the fellow used that word? Surely he had not surmised, from his manner, the crazy notion formulating in his mind? No, it happened to be the word for 'modest' that any man speaking a foreign language might use, meaning a quiet hotel.

He thanked the stranger, paid the bill, and went out into the arcades. The shops were closed for the lunch hour. The little town had grown very quiet. He made his way to the bridge over the river, stood a while examining the woody ravine into which the river plunged, and then walked along the leafy promenade in the direction of the Hotel Alexandra. When he came to it, it pleased him, with its shining white paint, its balconies, each with a gay pot of flowers and a little round table and canvas chairs. Every window looked on to the river.

He stood before it, uncertain, his mind racing with the idea that had begun to obsess him. The place was perfect for a romantic episode. Munich was only a few hours away. A telegram would be delivered this evening.

He turned away. Sheer madness! You, Aubrey Wellington, a famous musician, verging on sixty (well preserved and often taken for fifty), are playing with the idea of seducing a very young woman, a girl in fact, because she called early at your hotel, and walked and talked with you in all innocence, probably carried away, as so many are, by celebrity worship. No, one could not act in this fashion.

There was a pleasant little café next door to the hotel, with a terrace gay with tubs of flowers and little tables with coloured cloths. Several young couples were drinking coffee or eating ice-creams. Perturbed, angry with himself, he went to one of the tables, sat down and ordered an ice. He watched the young people around. They were so happy and twittered like birds in springtime. It was their springtime. His own time was autumn. The gulf of years lay between them. He watched their playfulness with envy but pleasure. They laughed with each other, Eros invisibly but patently present. One boy fed a red-lipped Amazon with close-cropped hair, and tight black trousers short over her vermilion socks. He gave her ice-cream on his own spoon. She swallowed it with round provocative eyes a few inches from his. The hand of a boy, strong, veinless and brown, imprisoned under the table a small white hand, their heads close together over a book they were examining.

He turned his face away. The music of youth mocked him. Sixty—but a charming young girl had risen early, crossed Munich to bid him farewell, and had kissed him of her own impulse! In the cage of Time might not a song burst forth from its captive, caught in a ray of sunshine?

He consumed his ice slowly. The boy with the open shirt and the dark curls had boldly thrust his mouth forward and taken the lips of the girl to whom he had given the ice-cream. Their eyes closed momentarily in Elysium, then they fell earthwards and withdrew from each other with a smile.

He turned in his seat and looked out across the river and the esplanade with its shady poplar trees. Afar, a mountain lifted its sunny flank to heaven, blue-creviced. The couples began to leave the tables, their lunch interval spent. He had an hour yet before the train left for Bolzano.

When he rose and passed the Hotel Alexandra again he noticed that it had no entrance on the river side. He took the next turning and came to the back street in which the hotel had its door. He would see what the place was like inside.

He went through the swing doors and found himself in a lounge, brightly decorated in the modern style. The reception desk was on the far side. A pleasant young man in a black coat came forward. Yes, he had rooms, single, double, or a suite.

"A suite?"

"Yes, sir. On the third floor, two single rooms with bathroom between, communicating."

He asked to see the suite. It proved to be bright, roomy and with a splendid panorama of the river valley at the foot of the great wall of snow-capped mountains. He explained that he could not take the rooms at once. "It depends whether my niece can join me. We would come Saturday morning for the week-end."

The reception clerk was sure he would have accommodation.

They descended to the vestibule. Wellington said he would telegraph from Bolzano as soon as he knew his movements.

"Very good, sir. You will be very welcome. May I have your name, sir?"

Wellington hesitated. He was about to say Brown, but before the name was uttered by him he realised the folly of such subterfuge. His passport would show his deceit. So he said, "Wellington—I am at the Hotel Greif, in Bolzano."

"Thank you. We shall hope to see you. Good day, sir," said the clerk, accompanying him to the door.

"Is there a telegraph office near?"

"Across the bridge, sir, on the opposite corner."

"Thank you."

He hesitated by the bridge. Should he or should he not? It was a crazy thing to do. She might rock with laughter, and show the telegram all round. "Look, Sir Aubrey Wellington has invited me for the week-end! What do you think it means?" "Oh, just another dirty old man! You'd be a fool to put your head in that noose!"

He could hear the chatter. But she would not show the telegram around. Why had she come to the station? Why had she kissed him? He could feel her warm lips on his cheek now, the intoxicating nearness of her fragrant youthfulness.

He paused on the bridge and watched the grey stream race under overhanging boughs. It gave a lyric note to the scene. It was a perfect setting for a mountain idyll. He thought of the young couple at the coffee-table, the youth holding the girl's hand, the yearning in their eyes as they smiled at each other. Very briefly, all too briefly, he had known those moments. Outwardly, a success, known the world over. Inwardly a failure, terribly lonely. Surely he had a right to a little happiness when it was offered him?

He might be all wrong about her. It might be just sheer hero-worship, a young girl's impulsive act. She might come, and there would be no fulfilment. He was prepared for that and would be decorous. The first move towards intimacy must come from her. He would be content with her fresh charm, her companionship. Would he? Yes. And the rooms at the hotel? He had observed that a separate suite could be made by bolting the bathroom door. But it would compromise her; there were their different passports. His niece? At a glance the reception clerk would know. Reception clerks knew a great deal. Like the three monkeys of Nikko they were trained to speak no evil, hear no evil, see no evil. He was building up a ridiculous fantasy. She might not come, she might not be able to come. But here was the place and the opportunity. Here might be enacted an idyll, the brief ecstasy of an Indian summer—if he had the courage to test his fate.

He crossed the bridge and sent the telegram. *Can you spend week-end Hotel Alexandra, Merano. Through carriage arrives noon Saturday. Reply Hotel Greif, Bolzano. Aubrey Wellington.*

"When do you think it will be delivered in Munich?" he asked.

"This evening," said the clerk.

He walked to the station to take the train back to Bolzano. Had he not seen that flower-girt chalet in the mountain promenade with *Zimmer zu vermieten* he would never have embarked on this folly. This idyllic place, perhaps the mountain air, had gone to his head. But surely she had started it?

All the next morning he awaited her reply. He would not make any excursions, but hung around the hotel. The lunch hour arrived. Nothing. All through the afternoon, nothing. He dined outside that evening in the trellised enclosure on the piazza. Nothing. He learned at the desk that telegrams were delivered up to ten o'clock. The hour struck in the church belfry across the square. Nothing. At eleven o'clock he went up to his room. He had made an utter fool of himself. She was not replying. Of course she was not replying. What effrontery! The dirty old man!

He looked at himself in the mirror. He was tall, slim, with an unlined face, but his hair, still thick, had greyed at the temples. He was what they always termed him in interviews "alert, distinguished". They might have added those hateful words "well-preserved". As he undressed the long mirror confirmed that he had retained almost a boy's figure. But there were tell-tale marks; his knees were a little saggy. Men over thirty-five should never wear shorts. He never did. And above the loins the flesh had subsided a little, leaving creases when he bent. His chest was hairless. He had always been well made and careful about his posture. There was not a suggestion of a loose stomach. He sometimes wore a pair of trousers made in Savile Row when he was twenty-eight. Nevertheless, he was sixty on Monday. Anne was twenty-four. Thirty-six years' difference. He could easily be her father. It was a good thing she had not replied, he thought, as he cleaned his teeth, all his own. He hoped she had not shown the telegram around. Still, he was disappointed. She was so vivid in his mind, so entrancingly young and eager. Why had she come to the station, why had she kissed him?

He got into bed. Tomorrow night, Saturday, he would sleep in the Villa Tiberio, alone as always. He would hear Miss Porritt talking to the maid the next morning before the breakfast-tray went out to the terrace, where she would await him, almost annoyingly bright at that hour.

"Did you have an enjoyable time, Sir Aubrey?"

"Very. A pretty young girl came to my hotel at seven-thirty, and kissed me as the train left."

He could imagine her face and comment.

"Oh, Sir Aubrey! You do tease me!"

He turned out the light, but was a long time getting to sleep. Surely she had got the telegram, it was the proper address? She might have gone away, but that did not seem likely. One did not go away on a Thursday.

He heard the clock across the piazza strike one. Then he slept.

He breakfasted the next morning in his room and packed. The station was only a few minutes away and the porter would carry his bag. He went downstairs and settled the bill. He remembered he wanted some shaving-cream. There was a chemist across the piazza. When he came back the hall porter said: "A telegram for you, sir."

He collected it at the desk. His hand trembled a little as he opened it. Well, she had replied. It would be No. He opened it. It was Yes. *Arrive noon train Merano. Anne.*

III

There was a bus leaving for Merano in a few minutes. The porter took his bag across to it. It was a grey morning, with a threat of rain. He was at the Hotel Alexandra before eleven. The rooms were vacant.

"My niece arrives at noon. I am meeting her."

"Very good, sir."

The clerk showed not the slightest surprise. My niece. What else could he say? Miss Beveridge, a young friend?

That would be stupid. The clerk could accept her as his niece, or not. He could have an American niece. Cardinals had nieces, business men had lady secretaries. A lie by any other name would sound as sweet. It was not likely that Anne would object. She would realise it obviated any speculation.

He went early to the station. The train was prompt. He felt momentary anxiety when he failed to see her. She was on the platform, carrying a small bag, before he found her. She wore a green felt hat and a raincoat. She had got down from the third-class coach. She came up to him, laughing.

"Aubrey!"

"Anne!"

He turned, and she kissed him at once, as their hands met. Then he took her bag.

"I was looking for you up in the second-class."

"I always travel third, poor-student-class—and it's so much more fun!"

They passed through the booking-hall, out into the great green square in front of the station with its background of forested hills.

"Oh, how lovely!" she cried.

"It's going to rain—shall we walk, it's only a few minutes."

She linked her arm in his, and looked into his face, her eyes dancing.

"I didn't get your telegram until late last night. I was out all day."

"I sent it Thursday afternoon—they said it would arrive that evening."

"It came at nine o'clock yesterday morning. When I got in last night my landlady had pinned it on my door. I ran all the way to the telegraph office and only got inside before closing. Did you think I'd jilted you?"

"No—I thought you had gone all round the campus saying, 'Look what I've had from that dirty old man!'"

"Aubrey darling! You're not old and you're not dirty. You are a famous, delightful young man! I'm lucky and

proud to know you. I wanted to show everybody the telegram, but I didn't! I kept my mouth shut."

She stood still, looked around her, and then gazed into his
eyes, her own very clear and blue under the absurd little
green felt hat with a cock's feather.

"Oh, Aubrey, what fun to be here! I can't believe it!
I thought I should never see you again!"

"Did you particularly want to?"

She made no answer, leaned forward and kissed him
solemnly on the lips. They walked on. The rain began to fall,
heavy black clouds obscured the mountains. They saw but
they did not care.

They came to the hotel. The reception clerk bowed. "May
I have your passports, please?" he asked.

"When we've unpacked."

"Thank you. This way, sir."

Key in hand he led them up the stairs to the second floor.
Their suite was at the end of the corridor. He opened the
door leading into a little vestibule. On either side were the
doors of their bedrooms. The bathroom separated these. The
porter carried Anne's bag into the room on the left. He had
taken the right one. There were flowers on her dressing-table,
placed there by his order.

The reception clerk opened the french window to show
her the balcony.

"Oh, how wonderful!" she exclaimed ecstatically.

The clerk withdrew. The door closed.

"Well?" he asked, when they were alone.

"Aubrey, it's perfect!" She glanced around. There was a
double bed with a single pillow, a bedside table with a
flounced shade, a kidney-shaped dressing-table with side
mirrors, a large walnut wardrobe, a chaise-longue, and an
easy chair in plum-coloured velvet. It was a woman's room.

"And your room?" she asked.

"Come and see."

They crossed the vestibule. His room was smaller, with a

single bed. A french window opened on to the same balcony. They stepped on to it. She laughed.

"What amuses you?"

"If I bolt my door you can come in by the balcony!"

"May I?" he asked.

"Don't be silly. I shan't bolt my door!"

They stepped inside and in a moment they were in each other's arms. She kissed him with abandon. Presently, she drew back her head and looked earnestly at him.

"Are you surprised at me?" she asked, her eyes searching his face.

"Amazed! I still believe I'm dreaming."

"Let's dream."

"You were surprised by my telegram? Whatever did you think?" he asked.

"I was surprised—and I wasn't. I haven't thought about it at all. I terribly wanted to be with you—and here I am!"

"But why?"

She made no reply for a moment. Then she put her hand up and ran her fingers through the hair on his temple.

"Aubrey, you mustn't be psycho-analytical—that's an American folly. I loved you at sight, and longed to be with you."

"At what moment did you feel like that—when we said good night at the hotel, or when we said good-bye on the platform?"

"Oh, long before that—long before you knew I existed or was looking at you! I watched you conduct at the opera, I heard you lecture, and I sat back at the Professor's party and heard you talk, and you grew and grew on me! Aubrey darling, don't be so serious!"

She ran her hand right through his hair, gazed at him a moment, and sealed his lips with hers, soft and warm against him. They stood like that for some moments. They could hear the river running over its stony bed. Then she gave a deep sigh.

"Anne, what on earth do you see in me?" he asked, breaking the silence.

"Someone I want to love me, someone I love."

"At my age?"

"I don't like boys. Oh, Aubrey, don't cross-examine me too much! Just love me, darling!"

He made no answer and held her in a tight embrace, her hair against his cheek, the scent of her like the breath of spring.

After a pause she said, "Don't think me a little pig, but I'm awfully hungry. I've had nothing since six o'clock this morning."

"Of course you're hungry. How thoughtless of me! We'll go down to lunch."

She opened her dressing-case, and took out a small satchel, flourished it, and went into the bathroom. He went out on to the balcony. The sun had come out again and the river valley laughed up at him. Was it possible she was here because of him? It left him a little dizzy. His wild throw with fate, against all discretion, had been rewarded.

A few minutes later they went downstairs. They gave the concierge their passports. Hers was conspicuously different, slim and green against his, fat and blue. They were ushered into the dining-room and given a small table by the window, with a view of the promenade. There were only four couples in the room. Obviously it was out of season. So much the better. He had feared someone might rise and greet him.

The food was excellent. They decided to take their coffee at the café next door. It was so gay with its coloured cloths on the tables and the striped sun umbrellas.

"Do you see that table, with the boy in a turtle-neck sweater, and the girl in a print *dirndl*? It was a couple at that table, so happy in love, that emboldened me to send you the telegram."

"Did you debate it a lot, Aubrey?"

"Round and round, until I was dizzy. And you?"

"Not for a moment. I rushed off to the telegraph office. You must think me a hussy."

"I think you're adorable!"

They held hands under the table, just as the young couple had done two days ago.

Later he showed her the little town. They visited the Gothic church, the tiny castle museum, the fifteenth-century residence of the Counts of Tyrol. Then they took the rack-and-pinion lift up to the Tappeiner Weg, the promenade high up above the town, with its trees, flowers and panorama of the snow-capped mountains. Presently he halted her, and pointed to the chalet with its geranium-laden balcony and overhanging roof. The sign *Zimmer zu vermieten* was still out.

"It all began there! It seemed built for our idyll. They advertise rooms to let, so I went in scarcely realising what I was doing. I was relieved when they told me they had no rooms! But the idea was planted there. No, that's not correct. You began it!" he said.

"Eve again?"

"Eve again. Why did you suddenly kiss me on the platform at Munich?"

"Because I had to. I loved you, and you were vanishing. I was surprised at myself."

"Do you often fall in love like that, as quickly?"

It was a foolish question and he regretted it the moment he asked her, but she showed no embarrassment or resentment. She made no reply for a few moments, as if pondering. Then she said, with an intensity that surprised him, "I didn't know then how much I loved you, how very much. I don't love easily, there's a reserve has always held me back, but with you I never felt for a moment like that—you were there and you were you."

She looked into his eyes as she spoke, unusually grave.

His hand sought hers, and pressed it.

"I am a little frightened," he said. "I may be a disappointment."

"If you are, the fault would be mine," she responded. "There will be no disappointment. I love you!"

They came to a seat, placed for its view, and sat down. There was a silence between them until she turned her face towards him, and said, "Do you think two lovers as happy as we are now, Aubrey, ever sat on this seat?"

"I hope so," he answered. "I only hope they are still happy."

"You think it can't continue—at the peak?"

"Well——"

"Of course it can't," she said, cutting across his caution. "But if you've touched the peak the memory of it's there for ever! Nothing, nothing can ever take it away!"

The intensity of her words made him regard her wonderingly. She had a child's frankness of mind, it went with her great simplicity. He made no reply. The long experience of life debarred him from so transparent a certainty. He felt very tender towards her innocence and remained silent. It was an innocence that disarmed him, and made the years and all their debris in his mind a profitless lumber. Presently they walked on. The promenade was deserted. Eden was their own domain.

IV

During dinner the rain came. The heavens opened and sheets of water deluged the town, dancing with silver spears on the pavement outside. It drummed on the glass roof and streamed down the windows. There was no sign of abatement; the storm was torrential.

They sat in the lounge for a while and lingered over coffee. A clock surprised them with Westminster chimes. It struck nine.

"Shall we go upstairs?" he asked.

"Yes—I'll have a bath."

On gaining their rooms they switched on the lights. The rooms looked cosy under the pink shades. The beds were turned down. A dressing-gown and nightdress, snowily flimsy, lay on her bed. A pair of red silk slippers looked like a child's.

"Aubrey darling, will you run my bath, not too hot?"

He went into the bathroom. Would the water run hot? Hot plates, hot water were the touchstones of a good hotel. The plates at dinner had been hot and the food excellent. He turned the tap. The water came hot in a few seconds. When the bath was full he went to his room and began to undress. After he had put on his pyjamas he walked restlessly about the room. It was still pouring outside on the Kurhaus promenade. He sat down and picked up a new biography of Richard Strauss which the Professor had given him, but the words meant nothing. He stood up again and looked out of the window. The day had now gone. On the opposite bank of the river the chimney-pots stood black against a sky, white, threatening, storm-wracked. They recalled other chimney-pots, the level orderly regiment of them, like a black comb, visible from his old London apartment, where a fourth-floor bedroom window looked westwards over the Brompton Road. How far away in time and place that was! London in his first years of marriage, a London that had not been visited by the bombs, devaluation, and a social revolution more thorough than the French Revolution, though quiet and bloodless.

He drew the curtains. How long would Anne be in the bathroom? He walked across to her room. A chair was littered with her lingerie. It was so feminine, so frothily delicious and entrancingly fragile. By contrast it provoked a thought of Miss Porritt's formidable exhibits on the line behind the potting-shed at the villa. Her garments were plainly utilitarian.

He was musing when a voice surprised him.

"There's a man in my room!" said Anne.

She stood in the doorway, enveloped in an enormous bath-towel. Her silver flaxen hair was wet, and darkened by the water. Her throat, shoulders and feet were bare.

"I feel I'm in the nursery," he said. "You're just a naughty child, you haven't dried yourself properly."

She moved forward into his arms. The scent of her, warm, fresh, took his senses. As she turned her head sideways on his shoulder he bent and kissed the damp flesh of her throat. Then their mouths met and a silence enclosed them. Presently he carried her to the chaise-longue.

"The light," she murmured, as he bent over her.

He stood up and switched off the light, leaving only the small rose-shaded lamp on the dressing-table. Closing the door, he went towards her as she lay there, her ruffled boy's locks fair against the maroon silk cushion. He knelt down beside her, and as she put up her arms to him the bath-towel fell away.

She lay smiling softly, a swan in flawless repose, curve on silken curve. His eyes caressed her.

"Psyche from the bath," he murmured. "Oh, Anne, you exquisite child!"

She smiled at him, and her hands went over his shoulders. With a cry he enfolded her, straining her to him, his face finding the tender refuge of her bosom.

v

Perhaps the silence woke him, for the rain had stopped. He saw by the bedside clock that it was almost two. Anne lay on her side, her face towards him, quietly breathing, her long-lashed eyes closed. He cautiously withdrew an aching arm and began to ease himself from the bed. A detaining hand moved to his bare shoulder. He kissed her softly.

"Good night, my darling."

"Stay," she murmured and, turning, pillowed her head on his chest. His mouth touched the soft crown of her head, one arm found the curve of her waist. Together, they floated away on a soundless tide of sleep. The rain, falling again, was unheard.

VI

He was not the first to wake. He opened his eyes in the dim room and found her looking down at him, the flaxen shock of hair framing her face, her slim white shoulders and breasts shining above him. He drew her down and slowly kissed the beauty revealed by dawn.

"Good morning, darling," he murmured.

"Good morning, Sir Aubrey," she said puckishly, shaking back the curls of her hair.

"What day is it?"

"Sunday—don't you hear the bells?"

He listened. The sound of bells came across the valley.

"What time is it?" he asked, lying in utter content.

She glanced at the bedside table. "Nearly nine o'clock."

"Gracious, we must get up!"

"No—let's snoozle. I love snoozling!"

She curved her body into his, and sighed.

"Puppy-dog," he said, and playfully bit the lobe of her ear. "Happy?"

"M-m-m," she murmured. "Divinely happy, darling! Let's lie here for ever. No more lectures, no more examinations!"

"No more operas, no more symphonies."

"That won't do—you have a public."

"The public be damned!"

"Naughty," she said, putting a finger on his mouth. He bit her finger, their eyes deep in each other. They lay then without talking, in a warm, blissful half-consciousness, utterly at rest, a sense of levitation taking them out of their bodies.

They must have slept again. It was ten o'clock when they woke. He slipped out of bed and into his dressing-gown. Then he sat down on the bedside and teased her into wakefulness.

"Do you want the bath?" he asked.

"It's big enough for two."

"You have a shocking candour for a young lady!"

"You have a quite unnecessary hypocrisy, Sir Aubrey. But you are English. I'm just an American barbarian!"

"You're adorable. I have never loved America more. Now I must leave you. I've a little deceit to practise."

"Deceit?" she asked, putting her arms behind her head, as she lay back on the pillow.

"I must rumple my bed."

"Isn't it silly—we could have had one room."

"Well, the economy doesn't matter. And I wasn't certain."

"Wasn't certain I would sleep with you? Despite my telegram?"

"Yes."

"That was tactful and sweet of you. I might have bolted you out?" she asked, with mock seriousness.

"But you didn't," he retorted, and stooping, kissed her impish young face.

"Now you must go. Pass me my dressing-gown," she said.

He picked it up off the chair and gave it to her.

"Lucky dressing-gown," he said, "to be so close and to enfold her."

"Darling, you do say pretty things. Are you sincere?"

"Not a bit. I'm just an old Casanova."

"I love my old Casanova!"

He put her red slippers by the bed. His own lay by the chaise-longue, he recovered them, then he shook out the bath-towel left there when he had carried her to bed. He laughed as he folded the towel.

"Why do you laugh?" she asked.

"I don't think I can tell you. It's a very silly thing."

"What is it?"

"A memory of Mrs. Pat Campbell."

"Who was she?"

"Darling Anne, how refreshingly young you are! Who was Mrs. Pat Campbell? That dates me! She was a very famous actress when I was a boy about town. She shook

London in a Pinero play, as Paula, in *The Second Mrs. Tanqueray*."

"What was it about?"

"Well, it was the story of a lady with a notorious past. Mrs. Pat was a beautiful and very witty woman. Her sayings went round London. We've rather fulfilled one of them."

"How?"

He knelt on the bedside, and tweaked her nose. "She once said that she'd gone from the hurly-burly of the chaise-longue to the deep content of the double bed. So have we!"

Anne rippled with laughter.

"You idiot-boy! Get off my bed. I want to get up."

"At your service, madame. Madame will have the tulle Dior, or the crêpe-de-Chine Patou?"

He blew her a kiss and went.

VII

It rained nearly the whole of Sunday. Around noon they took a walk along the river, in a clear spell. As they drank an apéritif in the Kurhaus gardens the sun came out, briefly but strong. They were so happy, so conscious of their happiness that they wondered if everyone around them knew.

"We must be more careful, or they'll see we are in love. I'm sure our eyes give us away! The waiter at dinner last night smiled at us. Do we look like honeymooners?" asked Anne. "We are so outrageously happy, aren't we!"

"Outrageously, and I don't care a fig, if you don't."

He caught her gloved hand and pressed it. "It's a happy place. John Galsworthy came here, and wrote part of a novel. He loved it. Richard Strauss, too, and the Empress Elizabeth of Austria."

"And now Sir Aubrey Wellington," she added. "I wonder if it will inspire you?"

"I feel inspired. I feel like a young god on Olympus!"

"And what am I?"

"Hebe. She had the power of restoring gods and men to the vigour of youth."

"I was Psyche last night—but I don't mind what I am if I can live with you on Olympus. We must make all the other gods and goddesses terribly jealous. They will do us mischief. No one can be so terribly happy without disaster."

He looked at her. The gaiety had gone from her voice. Her face was solemn. She was silent for a few moments, then she spoke, her eyes on his face.

"It's all quite wrong, isn't it? But why? Who started the idea that one cannot be in love, and know ecstasy, as we do? We don't rob or hurt anyone!"

"There are many mysteries which we should leave mysteries. You remember the story of *Cupid and Psyche*?"

He smiled at her, and was distressed to see tears in her eyes.

VIII

They lunched quietly, the only couple in the dining-room. He had a surprise in the afternoon. She saw some manuscript scores among the papers on his table. It was a work of his, long incomplete. There was a piano in the dance room and she insisted on his playing the unfinished composition. He discovered she was a skilled sight reader. The musician in her was a revelation. He should have known, but this volatile, enchanting child had completely masked the serious student. It set him wondering. He had never known such ecstasy as this. Neither of his marriages had approached it. It was not only the perfection of their physical harmony; a new life flowed through him, tranquillising yet stimulating. He found he could talk to her on the plane of his life's dedication. He speculated on what his life might have been had early manhood known this quickening influence. His was not only the desire of an ageing man to hold her elusive youth; he was aware of something more, something beyond a definition in physical terms. His dry triumph would have flowered in the warmth of her enthusiasm.

IX

When, after returning on Sunday night, she spoke of the train she was catching on the morrow, he said, "Anne, you cannot go!"

"Aubrey, I don't want to go, but I must! I have a lecture I must attend on Tuesday morning."

"Darling, you can't go tomorrow, for a very special reason."

"What is it?"

"It's my birthday tomorrow. I want consoling," he said. "We will have a special dinner. Of all my birthdays, this will be the most memorable. You'll stay?"

She made no reply but put her arms round his neck and kissed him. Presently, as they lay together, she said, "It's nice of you to have a birthday for me, but I've nothing to give you."

"You've given me yourself. No man on his sixtieth birthday ever had a present like that."

"Darling, don't be ridiculous. Fifty, I'd agree on. Sixty's a fable!"

"Beloved child, I remember Queen Victoria!"

She gazed at him, her fingers smoothing his greying hair. "You have the heart and body of a boy," she said gravely.

"Thank you—the schoolgirl's dream!"

"This schoolgirl's dream."

They both avoided the subject of their meeting again. She was going back to America, to California. He had thought of marriage, perilous though it was. His good sense counselled him to silence. No one could continue on this height of happiness, certainly not a man of sixty and a young woman of twenty-four. In ten years he would be seventy, and, if alive, slowing up. She would be thirty-four, in the full flood of life. Apart from the impossibility of her accepting, he realised the folly of such a dream. When Tuesday morning came they would part, with much anguish, aware that a fairy-tale had closed.

There was no shadow over their birthday dinner the next night. He found a restaurant, with zither music. There was a little present for him, some mother-of-pearl cuff-links, and he had found a parting present for her, a clasp in the form of a bird, in blue stones.

"The Blue Bird of Happiness, and it can't fly away," he said, pinning it on her breast.

It was midnight when they walked to their hotel, over the black-and-white pattern of the moonlight flooding the arcaded streets. They talked very little and were soon asleep. Her train left at nine o'clock. It was raining heavily when they got up, and the downpour continued all the way to the station. They preferred it so. All Merano should weep for them. With only a five-thousand-lire note in his pocket, he took her proffered five-hundred for the taxi fare. The train was in. She climbed into the third-class compartment, wearing again the little green felt hat with the cock's feather. And that was his last sight of her, her sad-happy face, looking out of the window, tears in her eyes, the green felt hat, her hand waving until she diminished from sight.

CHAPTER III

I

ALITTLE before one o'clock Wellington's guests arrived and were shown to the pergola. The American and his wife, Mr. and Mrs. Wesley Lane, were loud in their praise of Ligurio. They asked Wellington if he was composing anything.

"No—I've been almost barren now for three years. It may be I have finished for good. After all, I have composed a great deal. I feel entitled to retire," he said.

"But you will go on conducting, Sir Aubrey?" asked Lane.

"From time to time. I've just returned from Munich—we did *Die Entführung aus dem Serail*."

"I shall never forget your visit to Seattle, Sir Aubrey. I've never seen an audience so moved," said Mrs. Lane.

"You are very kind," he responded.

The Smolletts appeared on the terrace and came towards the pergola. He introduced them.

"Do you know that's the first time I've seen you in church for over a year?" said Tobias Smollett, his eyes twinkling with good humour. "What drove you there, my dear fellow? The desire for a good sermon? You know, I never preach sermons!"

"Before I answer your question, I'll ask one," replied Wellington. "What made you choose *The Song of Solomon* for the first lesson? Isn't it—er—unusual?"

"Very," agreed Smollett, his fine old face beaming. "Shall I tell him, Amelia?" he asked, turning to his wife.

She nodded. He referred to her in everything, and was under the impression that she always agreed.

"You see, I'm slipping badly. I get awfully muddled. I couldn't find the marker! Perhaps I didn't put it in, and while I was fiddling about, the Bible came open at *The Song of Solomon*. I haven't read it for fifty years or more. But I felt it was a little fortuitous, turning up like that. You see, next Thursday it's our Diamond Wedding. Old Solomon couldn't sing a Love Song like that! Could he, dear?" he asked, beaming at his wife.

"Why, Reverend Smollett, that's really wonderful! You've been married sixty years!" cried Mrs. Wesley Lane, holding out her hands to Mrs. Smollett. Then she kissed her on both cheeks.

"Sixty perfect years," said Mrs. Smollett.

"We came of age in the same year, and we married that year. But I wasn't quite prepared for old Solomon—a bit embarrassing, eh, in some parts? Having started, I had to go on!" said the chaplain. "Well, here's to you all!" he cried, raising the cocktail glass he had just taken from the tray.

"Here's to you, sir, and your good lady!" said Wesley Lane earnestly.

"And to you—to your next——" Mrs. Lane hesitated. "Wesley, what comes after a diamond wedding?"

"Silver, gold, diamond—that stumps me," said Lane.

"Possibly mink," said Wellington.

"Oh, what a good idea!" cried Mrs. Smollett. "I've pined for a mink coat for years. I've always had to wear parson's mink."

"What is parson's mink?" asked Mrs. Lane.

"Rabbit!" she answered gaily.

"You've not answered my question," said Smollett to his host. "What brought you to church this morning?"

"I know you think I'm Ligurio's leading infidel. The answer would be rather complex and embarrassing," answered Wellington. "I find one phrase ringing in my mind —*Many waters cannot quench love, neither can the floods drown it.* I jib at quite a lot of dogma, but I agree wholly with that."

He smiled at them all as he put down his glass.

"Why, Mr. Wellington, you look as if you've had a lot of happiness," said Mrs. Lane coyly.

"Yes, I have," he answered gravely.

Smollett looked at his host. He knew he had had two marriages, reputed to have been not very satisfactory. What did the good fellow mean? He seemed suddenly serious. It couldn't be anyone here in Ligurio. His mind ran over the colony. He could not think of a possible starter.

"Ah," he said, puckishly, turning to the Americans, "you must know that all the ladies adore our host. He floats about the world on a flood of admiration."

Giovanni appeared on the terrace in his white jacket and gloves.

"Lunch is ready, let us go in," said Wellington, feeling he had given himself away.

II

His mind had no rest all Monday and Tuesday. He should have felt ashamed, contrite, unhappy after his secret episode. Instead he had a sense of enormous well-being. His only deep regret was that something unbelievably wonderful had gone out of his life for ever. Anne had given him her American address, and had promised she would write. Would she; should he? Was it not wise to close the chapter finally? It was a fairy-tale that could have no sequel. In time she would meet some nice American boy. Lucky lad to have the years in hand with such a girl.

III

Early in the still morning of Thursday, with the dawn just breaking over a glassy sea, he woke. He was so clearly, so immediately awake that he had the illusion she had come into the bedroom and had spoken to him. She spoke to him with ten bars of music, springing complete, like Pallas Athene, from the godhead of creation. He rose and went down through the dim silent villa, clad in his dressing-gown, to his study in the east wing. Through the wide windows he saw a rim of silver light along the sea's horizon. He opened the french window on the silent terrace. The scents of dawn came from the sub-tropical garden below. He took some scored paper and a pen from his desk and went to the piano. The first ten bars, so clear within him, were tried and transferred to paper. He worked on with tremendous concentration and when, about eight, Miss Porritt opened the door he was not conscious of her. She knew the signs at once. She had seen him possessed of his dæmon. She went out without a word, and ordered breakfast to be taken in on a tray and left on the Moorish stool.

For two weeks he saw no one. Miss Porritt took complete charge. She turned away all visitors, answered all calls, hoarded all his letters. She heard the piano in the morning, in the afternoon and late into the night. She heard him pacing up and down the terrace outside. He answered questions without really hearing what was said to him or what he said in reply. Sometimes he slept on the couch in the study, sometimes in his bed. In the night Miss Porritt would wake, see a light streaming across the terrace, and hear, intermittently, the piano.

Thus was born the symphony that crowned his career, the symphony played in the following years by orchestras in all the auditoriums across the continents, the exquisitely lyrical *Merano Symphony*. It was his swan song, and he poured into it the artistry of a dedicated life.

IV

For two weeks Miss Porritt kept back his letters, as he desired on these occasions. There were thirty-seven. One morning he slowly waded through them. He put aside the private letters, the "fan" mail. He dealt first with the business letters. He opened a royalty statement from his agent. In these last twenty years, since world-wide recognition had come, he had had no money worries. But with a Greek sense of Fate over him he could not live in an ivory tower. He knew how many of his fellows, on whom the fickle goddess had not smiled, desperately lived. Each year he set aside twenty per cent of his income for the many needy cases brought to his notice. He had founded two musical scholarships; even so, he had never been inconvenienced. His needs being very simple, he was easily solvent, for if one worked one had little time to spend. It was the retired who should have increased, and not reduced, incomes, since they had more leisure in which to spend them. And some people would always be insolvent.

Miss Porritt, for instance, so wonderfully efficient in every way except with her own finances. She had muddled away her small patrimony. She always lived in advance of her income. Time and again he came to the rescue. Her disease was incurable. It was unfortunate that the casinos of Monte Carlo and San Remo were so near. Every month when her cheque was due she went like a moth to the candle. She had even economised on her clothes in order to enrich the casinos. He could not scold her too harshly. She had a reckless zest for life, and she would come through somehow. A kindly Fate often provided a number of Wellingtons to look after the Porritts.

The business letters disposed of, he turned to the private mail. One letter, in a strange hand, bore a Paris postmark. He opened it. The address and the handwriting conveyed nothing, and he turned to the signature at the foot of the single sheet. His heart seemed to stop at the sight of the bold short name he found there. Anne.

HOTEL HENRI QUATRE,
PARIS
April 4th

"DARLING AUBREY,

Here I am in Paris. I take the boat-train to Cherbourg in the morning for the *Île de France*. I seem millions of years and miles away from you. Europe will soon mean only one place for me, Merano, because there we were together, miraculously happy. Bless you!

ANNE."

The letter was a week old. She would be in America now. Slowly Time would do its erasing work in her young heart, the bright image of their brief happiness would become blurred. All life was before her, new faces, new experiences.

He read the letter twice. Then he very deliberately tore it into small pieces and threw it in the full waste-paper basket. He wanted to keep it, but that would be useless folly. Time bore too heavily upon him to hope that he could imprison the swift ecstasy of youth. He would never attempt that folly. Anne, too, had not blinded herself. He detected a note of finality in her brief message. She seemed aware, in her clear good sense, that miracles do not repeat themselves. She will not write again, he told himself. Perversely, he hoped she would.

He took a sheet of paper from the rack and wrote to her. The letter was longer than he had intended. He put it in the envelope, sealed it, addressed it to her San Francisco address, and added it to the pile of air mail for posting.

Towards noon when Giovanni came in to take the mail he called him back. He extracted a letter from his servant's hand. When he had left the room, he tore it into small pieces.

Book Two

OLD MEN FORGET

CHAPTER I

I

THE nonagenarian Mr. Crackenthorpe shifted uneasily in his pew. How could Tobias Smollett make such a fool of himself reading *The Song of Solomon*?

> *My beloved is gone down into his garden,*
> *   to the beds of spices,*
> *To feed in the garden and to gather lilies.*
> *I am my beloved's, and my beloved is mine.*

It might all be true enough, but you did not say such things in public. An allegory, certainly, but it seemed very close to the real thing. It was such a long time since he had gathered lilies, or adventured in the beds of spices. So very long. He still gathered a lily surreptitiously, but it was very cold and hard. There was a Carrara marble statue in his garden. It was a naked young girl, stooping on one knee, a hand delicately bent towards one breast. He loved that statue, the beautiful smooth thighs, the amphora-like belly, the twin breasts, small and virginal, and the sweet little head with hair drawn tightly up from the nape of the neck. He had bought the statue in Nice thirty years ago. He was told it was Calypso. Sometimes when he knew he was alone in the garden he stopped and ran his hand over the smooth thighs, the sunken navel and the pointed breasts. It was all very cold and hard, far removed from the warmth of life, as he remembered it, but he could not resist the sensation the contours evoked under his hand. As he caressed the nymph, he turned his head away for he did not like to see the black blood in the knotted veins of his hand, his senility emphasised by the smooth white marble. Who said that age had no

longing, that the ash held no warmth? Here was old
Smollett stirring the ashes.

He looked along the pews from the angle where he sat.
He surveyed Mrs. Gavin, like an old vulture with her blue-
lidded eyes; Maysmith, debonair as usual, ninety, his junior
by two years but shakier on his feet; Hugh Trent, eighty-one,
deaf and lame but still perky; Lady Crossley, brightly
efficient in everything; Mrs. Viviani who, though formidable
at the bridge table, had played her cards so badly in life; the
Countess Verdecampo di Saluzzo, an American, the most
beautiful woman of the foreign colony; Sir Aubrey Wellington, not really here, his mind far away, playing with the
twelve fundamental chords that enclosed his existence;
William Huddelstone, the retired Malayan planter, so
polite, so meek and ever-smiling, dragooned by a tartar wife,
and known as Sweet-William; Mrs. Dove, eighty-one, as
gentle as her name, with a weakness for gay hats; Miss
Dymphna Carter, who had been governess to an English
princess and lived with a litter of signed portraits of royalties
in her back bed-sitting-room at the Hotel Azalea; and, here
Crackenthorpe's gaze lingered, a new face, that of a pretty,
fair young woman accompanied by a dark, fresh-complexioned young man. Who was she, he wondered.

Many waters cannot quench love, neither can the floods drown it,
read Tobias Smollett in his mellifluous old voice.

That was true enough. His wife, dead now for four years,
whom he had bullied for twenty, increasingly assumed in his
memory the role of an angel. Many waters had flowed over
him in his ninety-two years, but the memory of that distant
love had not been drowned. He had no consciousness of the
tyranny with which he had ruled her, a victim of his irascible
temper. Every morning he put fresh flowers in front of her
portrait in the morning-room. She had died of bronchitis,
white-haired at seventy-four, but still rosy-cheeked, soft-
voiced.

Her voice. He was first aware of it one evening thirty-six

years ago in the convent-hospital near Florence where he lay near death. "I am praying for you, and you will live," he heard someone say in his half-consciousness. It was such a beautiful voice which spoke those words that he opened his eyes and saw a young nurse sitting by the bedside. He remembered then that he had been brought in from his Tuscan farm to the nursing home of the Blue Sisters. He was not a Catholic, but it was renowned for its nursing, and Catholics and non-Catholics were received alike. He could not remember how long he had lain there, and this was the first time since his entry that he had been aware of any living person. He stared at the young nun who had spoken, and he tried to talk but no words would come. It was then that something almost miraculous occurred. He saw tears fall down her cheeks, and as she bent towards him some of them fell on his hand. He was fifty-six and it was the first time that a woman had wept for him. A surge of emotion swept over him.

He looked at her steadily as she sat there, her head downcast, her hands folded in the nuns' manner of bead-telling. She was praying for him quietly, her eyelashes wet with the tears that had escaped her. It was a face of innocence, unlined, rosy and beautiful in its virginal contours, the round face of a girl who might have come off a farm. It did not, in shape or colouring, appear Italian, though she was a nursing sister in this Italian convent on the Fiesole hillside above Florence. The colour of her hair, fair with an auburn tint where he could just discern it beneath her coif, again suggested a non-Latin origin.

He could not, at that moment, see the colour of her eyes, for she was looking down in the static pose that never changed as she sat by his bed. He judged her to be about twenty-five. He would have asked her why she wept for him and why she prayed for him, a stranger, a man of fifty-six and, in her eyes, an infidel. But he was too weak for speech. He lay there, his mind bemused in its fatigue. Presently he slept.

In the following days he improved greatly. The same nun was at his bedside most of the day, being relieved in the evening by an older sister, and plainer. One morning he awoke to find his mind quite clear, his speech returned. When the young sister attended to him he spoke to her, and asked her name.

"Sister Maria."

"You are not Italian?"

"No, I am Irish."

"Are you a new sister?"

"No," she answered, "I've been here twenty-five years." Twenty-five years! It did not seem credible.

"You must have been a child when you came here," he said. For the first time he saw her eyes. They were blue and held a smiling light.

"I was seventeen. I came from Ireland, as a novice."

"Oh," he said, and was silent. Seventeen. Here twenty-five years. Then she was forty-two years old! It was scarcely credible. She had the smooth face of a schoolgirl. She was Irish. It explained the colour and softness of her skin, the auburn tint of her hair.

"I feel much better today," he said, after a silence. "You have been praying for me. Why?"

"We pray for everyone."

"And your tears—why did you cry for me?"

She made no reply to his question for a few moments. Then, straightening the pillow:

"You must not talk so much," she said, with her soft smile.

"Won't you tell me why you cried for me?"

"You were very ill and you were alone."

She looked at him gravely as she spoke and then left him.

They changed the nurse the next day. She was a robust middle-aged sister with a peremptory manner. On the fourth day, when he was allowed to sit up, he asked what had become of Sister Maria. He was told she was with another case.

"She came from Ireland. Has she really been here for twenty-five years?" he asked.

"Did she tell you that?"

"Yes."

"Then if she said twenty-five years, she has been here twenty-five years. I have been here only seven. We may not talk about one another," said Sister Aloysia firmly.

Reproved, he questioned her no more. On the morrow he was allowed to sit on the terrace in the warm March sunshine. Trees of golden mimosa flamed between the black cypresses in the hillside garden. There was a vista of the great dome of the Duomo and the tower of the Palazzo Vecchio rising from the city in the plain of the Arno. He had been a whole month at the Convent of the Blue Sisters and for a week had been gravely ill. "We nearly lost you," said his Italian doctor.

"When can I go home?"

"In a few days now."

He lay back in his chair, looking up at the blue sky. What a strange thing had he died! Death was something he had never thought about. They would have taken his body back to Ponte Arco, and there he would have lain in the cold north salon until they had brought out his only near relations, his sister and his cranky twin brother. They would have been very annoyed when they discovered that they had been by-passed in his will, although they had plenty, and that his fortune had gone to a great-nephew in Australia—whom none of them had ever seen, the grandson of his oldest brother drowned in the Pacific.

His estate at Ponte Arco, to which he would now be returning, consisted of a vast ruinous villa, once a monastery of which the fifteenth-century cloister with Benci frescoes was intact, and some two hundred acres of terraced olive-groves, in which were a dozen cottages for the peasants he employed. There was a sixteenth-century mill down by a swift stream that eventually found its way into the River

Arno. In this mill they crushed the olives and casked the oil. The groves and the mill were bought as a going concern, but the business had never been remunerative. His fortune was large enough to sustain the annual loss.

He loved the villa with its magnificent views of the Arno valley. He converted the old refectory of the monastery into a small theatre. Here he indulged his passion for music and drama. Any Italian workman who could sing or play an instrument well got a job on the estate. He imported as a manager a young Austrian who knew nothing about the oil business but was a born musician.

The musical productions at Ponte Arco became famous. The oil business went steadily downhill. As the revenues fell the expenses went up. The house was always full of those itinerant spongers who fatten on the follies of rich eccentrics. There was a phase when he was smitten with the theory of stage design promulgated by Gordon Craig. Two memorable productions by this wayward genius ate up a whole year's income in five nights. But it was a different disaster that shut down the theatrical era at Ponte Arco. At twenty-eight, after a month's courtship in Rome, he had married a beautiful Russian girl of twenty, the daughter of a ballet-master employed at the Opera House. Unfortunately, he soon found he had married a tigress. She had sudden rages in which she smashed the first things that came to hand. She made journeys into Florence and ran up outrageous bills for jewellery, dresses, furniture and fabrics. She refused to have children. She rose in the late afternoon and retired at dawn. After four years, distraught, and looking for some means of ridding himself of her, Fate played into his hands. She went off with his Austrian manager. Fearing she might return, he shut down Ponte Arco and went on a tour of the world. He was in Mexico City when he learned that his beautiful Olga had broken her neck on a bob-sleigh run at St. Moritz.

He came home to Ponte Arco. One-half of the patrimony inherited from his father, a millionaire sugar grower, had been dissipated. With a hatred of all women, he shut himself up in three rooms at Ponte Arco and became a miser and a hermit for the next twenty-two years. It was because of an economy of fuel in the cavernous villa throughout a bitter winter that he caught the chill that developed into pneumonia. He refused to have a doctor. When he was delirious the frightened Italian housekeeper, Elisa, who came in daily from the lodge, for he would not allow a woman to sleep in the house, called in a doctor. He was transported in an ambulance, unconscious, to the Convent of the Blue Sisters. The first thing he knew, on recovering consciousness, was that a young nun was sitting by his bedside and that she was praying for him while tears from her eyes fell on the back of his hand.

At the end of his first week of convalescence the doctor said that he could go home. For the first time he realised his position. Here he was, fifty-six, with plenty of money and no home. Ponte Arco and the slatternly Elisa was no home. It was cold, empty, silent. The fate of the bachelor had overtaken him, though he was actually a widower—"He lives like a prince and dies like a dog." He had lived like a prince, and had he died, he would have had a dog's funeral. Worse than a dog's, for it was the nature of that animal to tear the heartstrings of the human being who had loved him. Dogs often drew copious tears at their burial. He would have drawn none. There was his sister in France, separated for over thirty years from her husband. She had religious mania. She had progressed from Presbyterianism to Anglicanism, from Low Church to High Church, after a fierce parochial quarrel that landed her in a costly action for libel brought by a churchwarden. From the High Church she had gone to none at all, becoming a fervent peripatetic Buchmanite.

This phase had lasted three years, during which she bombarded him with pamphlets from an hotel in Switzerland. What transpired there he never knew. There was an explosion. Denunciations streaming from her pen, she had a "call" from a manipulator of Tara cards in San Francisco. Crackenthorpe heard from the family solicitor that this migration had cost her a great deal of money, for the Tara-card prophet was as skilful as other gentlemen who manipulated cards on a more mundane plane. She came back across the Atlantic with a mission—inspired now by Quaker leanings. At last she was of use to somebody. She bought a derelict château in France and turned it into a hostel for homeless French children. For two years there had been no communication from her. It was unlikely that she would have attended his funeral.

Nor would a tear have been shed by his brother, Sherman. A bachelor, he lived in a large house in the Midlands, crammed with pictures and bric-à-brac. A hermit, he kept two ancient servants and shut himself off from the world. Every Friday night he descended into the basement to check the gas, electric and water meters. The record, meticulously tabulated, went back for thirty-two years. He knew how many cubic feet of gas had been consumed in the Michaelmas Quarter of 1912. An analysis, with a graph over the same period, showed the rise and fall in the consumption of electricity. There were separate books for coal, milk, bread, laundry and groceries. On any week in any year, he could check the comparative cost.

At the side of the telephone in the study there was a box. When Henry visited his brother and wished to call up London there was a protest against his profligacy, although he was paying for the call. He paid also for local calls, putting twopence in the box by the telephone, and writing in the book the date, number and duration of the call. "One must keep a check on that thieving Post Office," said Sherman. When Henry observed that there were no entries for three months, Sherman replied, "We only have the telephone for inward calls."

It was in December, 1912, when Henry had last visited his brother. He was placed in a vast bow-windowed north room with twin beds, a marble wash-stand with ewer and basin, and an electric fire. The first night the fire was not on. The room was arctic. The second night Henry took the precaution of going to his bedroom, half an hour before he retired, to turn on the fire. When he went up to bed he was surprised to find only one bar was on. He was sure he had switched on all three. The third night he deliberately turned on each bar to find, on returning, that one bar only was on. This was too much. The next morning when the ancient Mildred brought in the brass hot-water can and drew the blinds, he admonished her. "Leave those bars on. This bedroom's an ice-box!" he said. The old maid looked at him meekly. "It's Mr. Sherman, sir, as turns them off. He doesn't like extravagance," she said.

"Then I'll pay for the damn' fire!" he retorted.

Long before bedtime the next evening he was brought to explosion-point. It was a lunatic's sense of economy, for his brother always opened a bottle of champagne and the table groaned under the weight and variety of food. In the drawing-room Henry could not see to read. There was a vast crystal chandelier, but only one small row had electric lights turned on. A faint shadowy light pervaded the room. It was a funeral parlour with all the pictures covered with blue silk shades to keep them from fading. The statuary was covered with muslin to keep off the dust.

"I can't see to read!" protested Henry. "Why on earth don't you have a small reading lamp by the fireplace?"

"Why on earth should I spend a pound putting in a plug in another man's house!" retorted Sherman.

His brother had taken a lease of the house at a fixed rent of fifty pounds for a twelve-roomed house, for forty years, in the most exclusive residential quarter of Merringham. The retort explained the long crack in the unrepaired drawing-room window-pane.

Henry banged himself down in the lounge under the chandelier and tried to read the evening paper. Sherman, as was his custom, disappeared into an attic that was his study. For thirty years he had laboured late into the night on the genealogical history of the Bentons, their mother's family. He ignored all the Crackenthorpes, having quarrelled with his father whom he hated. It was a *tour-de-force*. Eight hundred and seventy pages of genealogical tables, with footnotes, covering three hundred and eighty-two years of Benton family history, with accompanying coats-of-arms reproduced in colours by Sherman with marvellous precision. It transpired that only one Benton, by effort or chance, had ever approached any kind of distinction in three centuries of comfortable living. Great-grandfather Benton, something of an art collector with a private gallery in his house at Streatham Hill, had been a Master of the Worshipful Company of Skinners.

"It must have been in the blood. The old boy chose the right Company. He was a skinflint if ever there was one!" observed Henry one day, nauseated by Sherman's ancestor-worship in the female line. The remark was *lèse majesté*. Sherman never forgave him. He was a fervent Skinner. Once a year he went to London, at Corpus Christi, to attend a prodigious Company banquet, from which he returned with a large box of candies bearing the Skinner arms. The contents were ritually consumed on Sundays after dinner, and made to last until the next banquet.

Sherman's annual excursion to London involved in considerable expense. He stayed at a mouldy hotel in Woburn Place because he could walk to and from St. Pancras Station carrying his bag. The banquet was the only occasion on which he wore evening dress. The dress-shirt was wrapped in tissue paper, and was made to serve three dinners without going to the laundry.

Sherman had many hatreds, but his greatest hatred was directed towards politicians, and of all politicians in a decadent England ("It took the Roman Empire four hundred years to fall, the British Empire's done it in forty, sir!"),

Lloyd George was the chief culprit. Sherman had never forgiven him for his attacks on the House of Lords. "A fanatical Welsh hymn-singing attorney, sir!" he bellowed.

Sherman never ceased considering ways and means of reducing his expenditure. For some years he had subscribed annually to the Society for the Prevention of Cruelty to Animals. "Sir," he wrote to the local secretary, "in view of the constant reduction of the value of the currency, I am compelled to adjust my subscription. I am, therefore, with much regret, enclosing my cheque for twelve shillings, the true present value of the pound." Having taken it out of the animals, he took it out of himself. Every year he travelled to Italy for three weeks. He always went third-class on the boat, second on the train, and sat up all night. He carried sandwiches, the remains being as hard as a brick on his arrival at Rome.

Henry remembered one of these holidays undertaken with his brother when they were very young men. In a mood of great excitement they arrived in Venice. They retired to bed early the first night, having sat up in the train all the previous night. About two o'clock in the morning Henry was awakened by the sound of movement. The light was on and he was astonished to see Sherman, pyjama-clad, coming into their bedroom. "What's the matter?" he asked, sitting up. His brother held a pair of shoes in his hand. "I've just brought them in. How do we know these Eyties won't charge for cleaning them?" he answered, closing the door softly.

Sherman must now be worth at least a quarter of a million pounds. He certainly would not journey out to bury a brother unless all funeral expenses were paid, reflected Crackenthorpe, contemplating an unmourned death.

For the first time in his life, having been on the brink of eternity, he felt lonely and frightened. That was why he had been so surprised and moved by the tears of a little nun. She had prayed for him because he was very ill and alone. How did she know he was alone? Possibly because in all those weeks no one came, no one sent him flowers. He thought

of all the free meals and entertainment he had given at Ponte
Arco, the crowded "first nights", the parties with Olga
flashing like a heron, the week-end guests. No one of all that
host had sent a flower or made an enquiry.

Ponte Arco had been shut down for twenty years. Hermits
live in the prison of their loneliness. It was true that he had
not minded living alone, but now he was frightened at the
thought of dying alone. Not quite alone. The Sisters never
let a patient die alone. They came with a priest, hoping to
snatch a soul from damnation. They even watched by the
corpse day and night until burial.

His gloomy reveries on the terrace, his thoughts, in such
contrast to the brightness of this day of the early Italian
spring, were broken by the appearance of his doctor. Dr.
Politti spoke English fluently, a cheerful young man who had
set up a practice in a village near Ponte Arco.

"Now isn't this good," he said, sitting down beside him,
and removing from his neck the stethoscope he had just used
on another patient. He took Crackenthorpe's pulse, then
put down his hand.

"I think you can go any time now—but I don't advise
Ponte Arco. The wind's too cold yet."

"Then where?"

"I think you should go to the Riviera. There's an excellent
hotel, the Bellevue, just opened at Ligurio. I've sent a number of my patients there to convalesce. They all spoke highly
of it. Why not a month's convalescence there?"

He went, and thus Ligurio in which he had lived now for
more than thirty-five years had come into his life. He had
never returned to Ponte Arco.

Two days before he departed from the convent hospital
Fate was kind to him. Walking in the garden he discovered
Sister Maria reading her Breviary. She stood up at once,
greeted him and turned to go.

"I'm sorry to intrude—but please, a moment," he said.
"I have so much to thank you for, and after tomorrow I leave."

She made no reply, her eyes cast down in the traditional rule, her hands folded, with the small black Breviary between.

"You said I was alone—I am, and will always be, unless I find some person with whom I would like to pass my years —not so many, for I am fifty-six."

"I pray that God will send you someone worthy," she said quietly, her eyes still downcast.

"He has."

"Yes?"

She raised her face, a smile in her eyes, lit with surprise.

"He has sent me you," said Crackenthorpe. "Will you come back into the world, and be my wife, and let me cherish you?"

There was a long silence in which their eyes met. He saw her tremble, then recover herself. Someone was approaching.

"Yes," she said quietly. "I will be here again at six o'clock, for a few minutes."

She moved away, head bent, from the shadow of the alcove into the sunlight.

II

It had been as quick and simple as that, but the complications were immense. She was a nun breaking her vows. True, hers was not a closed Order, but she had renounced the world to become a bride of Christ.

In Florence, Crackenthorpe had a friend, a middle-aged woman, Signora Lombardi. She was a Scotswoman, whom he had employed for five years as a secretary at Ponte Arco. There, at one of the performances, she had met a young Italian lawyer, Enrico Lombardi, of a good Bologna family. They married and settled in Florence. Julia Lombardi was a sensible, solid woman, efficient in all she undertook. He now turned to her for assistance.

He moved into Florence three days after his proposal to Sister Maria. It was arranged that on the Thursday, when accompanied by Sister Teresa, with whom she was paired on these visits to Florence, Maria should call, for charitable purposes, on a lady at the Grand Hotel. She would leave there shortly afterwards in Signora Lombardi's waiting car and be driven to her home. The next day, after seeing Henry, the two women would proceed to an hotel in Milan where they would make a shopping excursion, in a store managed by a cousin of Enrico's. There the nun would exchange her convent attire for that of the lay world she was entering. The next day they would be married by the British Consul, and proceed at once to Ligurio. Henry Crackenthorpe had engaged a small suite at the Hotel Bellevue. No one in Ligurio knew them. No one, at their ages, would believe they were honeymooners, the bride a runaway nun.

The plan was fulfilled without a hitch. Sister Teresa, waiting in a corner of the Grand Hotel lounge while her companion went to the ladies' room, was surprised, after a quarter of an hour, to see a page approach and deliver an envelope with her name on it. She opened it to find another envelope addressed to the Mother Superior and a note, signed by Sister Maria, informing her that she should not wait any longer as she would not be returning to the convent.

In the store in Milan, in a private fitting-room, the nun's habit and all her clothing were exchanged for a complete trousseau suitable for her new life. It was a perturbing experience to change the nun's heavy corset and flannel petticoats for the flimsy attire of the world. She felt naked in the silk stockings that replaced the thick woollen ones, and insecure in her delicate pointed shoes after the flat, square-toed slippers she had worn for so many years. She could not accustom herself to holding up her head and not folding her hands demurely before her.

The discarded nun's clothing was made into a parcel and returned to the convent. The parcel contained the plain gold ring that marked her as a bride of Christ. This she had removed, with tumultuous emotion, and wrapped in tissue paper. She had done a most terrible thing, she had broken her vows and given a heavy blow to those gentle sisters among whom she had lived for twenty-five years. When she had first come among them she was a bewildered girl of seventeen, fresh from Ireland. An unhappy home and an importunate priest, abetted by a mother worn down by a household of five daughters and three sons for whom her lazy husband could not provide, had resulted in her taking the veil. After a miserable brief noviceship in a cold Irish nunnery, the nursing order of the Blue Sisters with its noble service to the sick became her goal. Her first task, a shy Irish girl, had been to keep watch alone all one night beside the corpse of a man of seventy. He had died of dropsy and his limbs kept adjusting themselves by subsidence under the grey shroud. With a great effort she refrained from screaming. The nun relieving her at dawn found her shaking as with ague. It was her first and indelible experience of death.

The years slipped by and with them came a growing unrest. It was in vain that she tried to suppress her enquiring mind. She severely tried the Mother Superior with some of her questions. She was not of a rebellious nature, and her belief was deep and unassailable, but, unlike the Sisters around her, she had reservations both in regard to doctrine and discipline. Slowly she had to admit that she had not truly a "call". It was a long and secret battle within her. It made her life difficult and she began to feel deceitful among these dedicated souls for whom she had affection and respect. She had never been in love. The convent life was not for her a refuge from disappointment. A member of a nursing order, she was not shut off from the world. She had human contacts.

Now, for the first time in her life she had felt a deep attraction for a patient. She could not analyse her interest in Henry Crackenthorpe. She scarcely knew why she had cried for him or was distressed by the loneliness that encompassed him. It was not wholly pity; she had felt pity for so many of the patients who came to the convent. When he spoke to her in the arbour that day and made his sudden proposal it seemed that this was her order of release, that she had a new task, to go out into the world and to love and serve this man who had offered her his heart.

Throughout the trials that assailed her in more than thirty years of married life she never regretted her choice. In the convent her name was dead for ever. All reference to her dreadful act was forbidden. When the parcel of her clothes came back they were burnt. It was as if they might contaminate a new wearer. The Church, so adaptable in its ancient wisdom, did not reject her. Later, she had a second marriage, a Catholic one, since she had been troubled by the thought that, in the Church's eyes, she was living in sin. In due time she received the mass and made confession. To the end of her days she was a devout and faithful child of the Roman communion.

As a husband Crackenthorpe had never sought to influence her religious belief, but he had no illusions about his position. He was a wolf who had raided the fold. Catholics, by whom he was surrounded, regarded him with amused tolerance, as a boy who had robbed the larder. A rich man, of sedate habits, he suffered no ostracism among her Catholic friends. He kept open house, his entertainment was lavish. Mrs. Crackenthorpe, lovely and gentle, was the favourite of everyone. There came a day at last when she, the runaway nun, and he, the Protestant husband, were received in audience by the Pope during a visit to Rome.

Their honeymoon was spent at the Hotel Bellevue. After a month, they began to consider buying a property and settling in Ligurio. It was the year 1915. The easy civilised world was to be shaken and disfigured by four long years of savage massacre that left Europe anæmic and undermined the age-long social order. In Ligurio a thousand of the English breed, moneyed, leisured, well-bred, and firmly entrenched within their social caste (a little beneath the Peerage, well within "the County" and strongly flanked by the Services), had for almost fifty years spread themselves over the mountainside and taken possession of the small seaside town. Ligurio, nestling in orchards of apple, pear, lemon and orange trees beneath the terraced olive groves that climbed the steep amphitheatre of hills, embraced a half-moon of golden sand. That sand was Ligurio's unique asset. The other resorts along the coast offered either rock or shingle.

An English Mæcenas had discovered this choice retreat in the early 'eighties. He bought land and built villas. Retired governors, admirals, generals, judges, naval commanders, colonels and their ladies spread themselves in the embowered villas on the cypress-dotted hills. There was a plentiful supply of cheap servants drawn from the towns and villages. The pound was paramount, a gold coin with the effigy of Queen Victoria or Edward VII, that outweighed and outshone the lesser breeds of foreign currency. The shopkeepers along the narrow street that threaded the little town, a section of the old Via Aurelia whose name still carried an aura of the vanished grandeur and power of Rome, learned to speak English with an eye to profit; this, in turn, supported the English in their determination not to learn any damn' foreign language.

They were easy spenders, vulnerable to all tricks, seduced by the smiling politeness of the natives. They became devoted to their Marios and Mariettas, and in due time rewarded them with annuities, legacies and properties. It was safe, profitable, and it conferred a prestige to be in the service of these monied *Inglesi*. Even a large crop of elderly spinsters of very limited means, but of unfailing graciousness, observed the rule of *noblesse oblige*, squeezing themselves to keep up a generous tradition. Soon the colony had exceeded a thousand, with three dozen titles, two ex-excellencies, five ex-generals and seven ex-admirals. A paid chaplain was imported, a large vicarage and a church were built, together with a club, library and tennis courts. Innumerable cafés

began to spring up, but one, Valentino's, drew the élite.
When the cocktail habit came with the decline of the caste
system, and everybody met everybody, it reaped a fortune.

Ligurio was quiet, clean, floral and not too accessible. The
motor charabancs had not yet arrived to destroy its seclusion. In summer Ligurio, like all its Riviera neighbours, fell
fast asleep. The English went home to England for three
months, the villas were all closed, nothing moved on the
road. The few who were too poor to go away, either to
England or up in the hills, hid themselves behind drawn
blinds and were not "at home". The era of fried flesh and
bikinis on the burning beach had not dawned. The Italian
beaches were left to the Italians, and these were only a few
native fishermen and beachcombers. The New Order, with
six in one bedroom, three in a bathroom, a hundred miles of
advertisement hoardings, one hundred thousand cars on the
Riviera highway, and one square yard of scorching sand per
person, lay in a crazy future. Ligurio had not yet achieved
one of its forty concrete skyscrapers, its twelve thousand
washbasins with hot and cold running water, its thirty
garages choked with shining slayers. A hundred well-condi-
tioned horses slumbered in old stables. In spring they wore
bright straw bonnets and drew lovely ladies in billowy
cotton frocks. Horses and donkeys stopped to drink at a
trough provided by the Misses Hope-Walpole. Mrs. Waddi-
love, the General's wife, who founded a branch of the
R.S.P.C.A., almost complained of a lack of ill-treated animals in Ligurio. She gave an annual prize of a horse-blanket
for the best-groomed horse and a new top-hat to its owner.
Everyone rode in carriages. There was no shortage of manure
for geranium pots.

It was to such an elysium of the English in power, now
threatened by a prolonged war, that Henry brought his
runaway bride. The story soon leaked out. The bride con-
quered Ligurio. She was demure, pretty, devoted. Henry was
regarded as a naughty but lucky old dog. Everyone believed

that Mary Crackenthorpe was twenty-eight and not forty-two. The bride still blushed. The years had been added to make old Henry less of a dog, they said.

Crackenthorpe looked for a villa in which to settle. While they were looking the widow of Colonel Kimbolton conveniently died. The Villa Escalonia was superbly situated. It nestled in an olive-grove four hundred feet above the town. It had a long terrace that commanded a view of the bay in its half-moon sweep between the two headlands. At night Ligurio jewelled the scene with its lights. The villa, reached by a winding drive, was built on stone arches, its green shutters folded back on the pink-washed walls. It had nine bedrooms, a long salon with a painted ceiling, a study, morning-room and dining-room. A Carrara marble staircase, a little too grandiose, led from a hall with a fountain and basin to the upper floor. It had been staffed by four servants, a gardener and coachman. Henry added another servant and a second gardener. In place of a coachman he installed a chauffeur. He paid for the property ten thousand pounds. It was considered a good figure. The new owners stayed at the Bellevue while a second bathroom and hot- and cold-water basins were installed in all bedrooms. Italy had not yet entered the war.

One morning on the breakfast table in their sitting-room at the Bellevue, Crackenthorpe placed a long envelope on his wife's plate.

"What is it?" she asked, as she sat down.

"Open it, darling," he said, moving her chair forward.

She opened the envelope, drawing out a long folded parchment document. It was the title-deed of the Villa Escalonia, which he had brought back the previous day from the lawyer in Genoa. The conveyance was made out in her name.

"Oh, Henry!" she cried. "But why in my name?"

He leaned over her chair and put his hands on her shoulders, kissing her.

"I thought it wise, darling. You are forty-two, I am fifty-six. I shall most certainly predecease you, and I want you to feel secure, apart from anything else I leave."

She got up, clasped the deed to her bosom and then embraced her husband.

A month later they moved into the villa. Life was an idyll. She looked and felt like a girl.

CHAPTER II

I

IT remained an idyll for ten years. They were happy. They were popular, and then they drifted apart. At sixty-four he began to grow deaf, obstinate and tiresome. For a long time, unwilling to admit his handicap, he refused to wear a hearing-aid. She had to shout at him until her voice was hoarse. He became increasingly difficult in many ways and seemed unaware of the disparity in their ages. Each year increased the strain of their relationship. He would cough loudly for hours, or get up in the middle of the night, or, in his deafness, bang windows and doors. Sometimes, in the early morning, he put on the light to read or began rustling about with papers or dropped things. A day came when she asked for a separate bedroom. There was a scene between them. He shouted and banged the table. Did she want to get rid of him?

A mild little priest visited the villa frequently. They both encouraged him to come. Father Crotti was an excellent pianist, a fervent disciple of Bach, whose music he played with professional skill. He was an expert chess player, for which game Henry Crackenthorpe had a passion. They had long duels, shut up in the study. It seemed, therefore, singularly outrageous when, during the outburst over separate bedrooms, he shouted—"I know who's behind it! It's that damn' little priest putting ideas in your head!"

She made no reply. Trembling and white, she left the room. Upstairs she had a heart attack and was in bed for a week. Their relations deteriorated. Ever more gentle, more quiet, she spent her time in the morning-room that looked on the terrace. He spent more time in the study. Despite his remark, he was miserable when Father Crotti could not get in for a game of chess. He began to haunt the bridge club, but he was such an irascible loser that he was tolerated rather than welcomed.

One day on his return from an excursion to Nice, he brought back a white Carrara marble statue he had found in an auctioneer's shop on the Boulevard Massena. It was French rather than classical in every line, carved with a Latin voluptuousness, embarrassingly nude and provocative. His wife protested against its position in the hall, the cause of another scene, and eventually it was transferred to a table in his study. The little priest always sat with his back to it when he came for a game of chess. "*Troppo nudo!*" he murmured to Mrs. Crackenthorpe.

A week before his eightieth birthday Crackenthorpe received a bad shock from Dr. Martini, brought in after a stormy scene with his wife over the household bills. She could not account for five thousand lire. He called her an incompetent fool. She had been exhausted in the search for a new parlourmaid and cook, to replace a pair who had walked out after he had called them to the table and thrown a whole tureen of potatoes out of the window, declaring that they were under-cooked.

"I must warn you, Mr. Crackenthorpe," said Dr. Martini, "that if you create any more scenes the consequences may be very grave for your wife. Her heart is in a very poor state. One more shock may be one too many, you may lose her."

"Get the hell out of here!" shouted Crackenthorpe. "It's my heart that'll give out, and wouldn't you all be pleased!"

"Indeed we should," responded Martini, with grave candour.

Crackenthorpe stared at him, stunned by this remark. "How you all hate me!" he said.

"No—we do not hate you. But you have a saint in the house and you behave like a devil. I'm sorry to speak like this, but there is nothing wrong with Mrs. Crackenthorpe except you. As for getting the hell out of here, the hell you make would still be here, and as long as your wife desires me to act as her doctor, I shall continue my visits to hell!" Having expressed himself forcibly, Dr. Martini departed. He was a much-beloved man in the English colony.

Crackenthorpe paced up and down his study, shaking with fury. Then he suddenly sat down. No one had ever dared to talk to him like that. He was quiet all day.

When Father Crotti came that evening for a game of chess he was so subdued that the little priest enquired if he was well.

"Padre, would you consider me a violent man?"

"Not violent, *mio figlio*—but *frustrato*."

"Frustrated—how do you mean? You don't believe in that damned psycho-analysis nonsense? How am I frustrated?"

Father Crotti moved a king, and slowly suspended his hand. Then he looked at his opponent, smiling behind the thick lenses of his spectacles.

"*Caro amico*, it is the flesh not the spirit that sins in you," he said quietly.

"What the hell do you mean?"

"You are too physically based," replied Crotti.

"Don't fence with me. What do you mean by that?"

"I mean, *caro mio*, that your carnal desires have not been sublimated."

"Are you inferring that I'm unfaithful to my wife, that I fool around with the housemaids?"

"Worse," said Father Crotti, smiling.

"How worse?"

"We would not condemn you too severely if you did take carnal pleasure of your housemaids, though it would be most regrettable and sinful. My Church has a deep experience of human weakness. We know there are husbands who find physical satisfaction on the side, for whom youth, or the excitement of a fresh conquest, is irresistible. They indulge themselves, and yet in a manner are faithful spiritually to their wives. They have respect and love for them, even while they err. But you are in a worse condition, you are mentally unfaithful. I have observed it with deep sorrow. It's your move, *caro*," said Crotti, lifting his hand.

Crackenthorpe sat back and made no move.

"You say I am unfaithful. If I told you that I have never been unfaithful to my wife, would you believe that?"

"Yes."

"And yet you say I am unfaithful. How do you make that out? What have you observed, 'with deep sorrow', as you put it?"

Crotti folded his hands over his stomach. The only vanity he indulged himself in was his hands. They were sensitive and beautiful. In the mass he used them a little theatrically, for the glory of God. He looked down at them now in a meditative pause.

"*Caro*, behind me there is a statue on your desk. I try not to see it but it obtrudes itself. It is naked, it is voluptuous in every curve. Its appeal is solely to the senses. The eye is a great sinner, it is the keyhole of evil vistas. I cannot help seeing that the nymph is highly polished where your hand lasciviously lingers. Rape is not always an act of physical lust, it can be mentally committed. If you are physically based and without spiritual discipline you can know no peace, you are shut off from the sublimation by which our natures are changed. Forgive me, I do not wish to offend."

"Have you said all?"

"Not all—but shall we go on with the game?"

"No," said Crackenthorpe shortly. "I want to get to the bottom of this. How the devil do you come by all this?"

"I am a celibate, being a priest, but the Confession teaches me a great deal about human frailty and its infinite complexities."

"That's what I can't stomach in you Catholics—monkeying about with our private affairs, poking your nose into what goes on between a man and his wife," said Crackenthorpe, his anger rising. The observation about the statue had stung him.

"Are you consulting me or attacking my Church?" asked Crotti, in a low, calm voice.

"I'm consulting you."

"Then let us leave out the faults of myself or of my Church. You wish me to go on?" he asked.

"Yes, have your say."

"Mrs. Crackenthorpe is a saint. She committed a grave sin——"

"In marrying me, I suppose?"

"Yes, but her life since that lapse has been one of long atonement. She has made her peace with the Church. In due time we gave our blessing to your union. Like too many marriages, it began in a romantic aura, but having called upon her for a tremendous sacrifice, which she made, you did not allow your union to take on a spiritual aura. Nothing can endure on that basis."

"And how do you know all this—has she complained?"

"Please, *caro mio*! I am not Signora Crackenthorpe's confessor. Had I been I would not have ventured to say what I have. I speak from observation. You have treated her, to the knowledge of many, like an aggrieved person. It has hurt me to witness your cruelty."

"Cruelty! My God, what will you say next!" cried Crackenthorpe, his eyes blazing.

"I say cruelty, *figlio mio*—not physical but mental. It wounds one much deeper."

"I wonder you set foot in this house since you regard me as a monster!"

"I do not regard you as a monster, only as a sinner."

"Look, my good padre, let's be frank. Are you suggesting I am getting to a point where I shall be apprehended for messing about with a young girl up a lane or monkeying with a housemaid?" demanded Crackenthorpe loudly.

Father Crotti slowly unfolded his hands and raised them in gentle expostulation.

"I will ask you a simple question and I hope you will answer it honestly. If without any fear of discovery or retribution you could 'mess about' or 'monkey', as you put it, with a young girl—in simpler form, if you were a kaffir king in a kraal—is that what you would like to do?"

"Good God, no!" cried Crackenthorpe.

"Then why do you caress that marble nymph—as a connoisseur of art?"

"You have the damnedest way of putting a question!"

"*C'est mon métier*, which a priest shares with counsel," answered Father Crotti, smiling. "Can you answer my question?"

There was a silence. Crotti's eyes gently held those of his host.

"I could, but I'm damned if I will!" said Crackenthorpe sullenly.

The beautiful hand descended and touched a piece on the board.

"Mate," he said quietly.

Crackenthorpe rose abruptly and walked across to the window, and stood there, his back to the room. After a few moments Father Crotti got up and went to him, placing a hand on his shoulder.

"*Caro Enrico*, you began by asking me a question. I have tried to answer it honestly. If I have hurt you, forgive me."

"You have a hellish way of getting under a man's skin, like all your tribe. You've got under mine, by God you have," said Crackenthorpe, looking at the priest. "There's nothing to forgive. I asked for it and I got it. I am a carnal monster, sick with frustration, lapsing into dirty senility, beyond praying for!"

"No human being is beyond God's mercy and Christ's redemption," said Father Crotti gently. "Shall we resume our game?"

Crackenthorpe made no answer but walked back and sat down in front of the board. The priest observed how his friend's hand shook as he moved his piece. They played earnestly for an hour.

II

Within one week Crackenthorpe had been badly shaken by the doctor and the priest. The latter, calling a few days later at the Villa Escalonia, had visible evidence that his words had had some effect. There, in an alcove at the top of the first flight of the garden steps leading to the portico, he observed the kneeling nymph. The outcast glimmered among the vine leaves. She seemed more appropriate in that Bacchic retreat. Father Crotti suppressed a smile. He was careful in the house to make no comment on the eviction. Did he detect in the old boy a gentler tone towards his wife? Certainly there was a change. His next call turned a doubt into a certainty. The chess table had been moved out of the study into the morning-room where Mrs. Crackenthorpe had spent so many lonely evenings.

"I think it's a little cooler here than in the study," observed Crackenthorpe as they sat down. Mary Crackenthorpe sat in her favourite corner busy with her *petit-point*. The room was cooler, but the atmosphere was warmer.

CHAPTER III

As his eightieth birthday approached Crackenthorpe became a reformed character. He checked his splenetic outbursts, he refrained from stroking the nymph in the garden, he spent more time in his wife's boudoir and was singularly affable to the friends who called on her. He started a new hobby. He discovered colour photography and, using his wife as a model, was delighted to find she was photogenic. Her colouring even now in her sixties was exquisite. It was delightfully exaggerated in the photographs he took. "My lovely Irish rose," he said, showing his studies. One morning when she had a slight heart attack and had to keep to her room he was distraught. "It's nothing serious?" he asked Dr. Martini when he came downstairs.

"The heart's always serious—but a few days in bed will put her right," said Martini, a little delighted by the old man's anxiety.

"She'll be up and about for my birthday party?"

"Yes—don't worry, she'll be up."

She was up several days before the great event of his eightieth birthday. On the actual morning it might have been her eightieth birthday and not his from the solicitude with which he now treated her. At breakfast that morning when she went to the table to wish him many happy returns and to kiss him, he was singularly moved and suddenly caught hold of her and burst into tears. "Mary, never leave me, never leave me!" he cried.

She comforted him like a frightened little boy.

It was a memorable birthday. Presents poured into the Villa Escalonia, a bower of flowers, ribbons and boxes. The party he gave that evening at the Hotel Bellevue was a

memorable event. Ligurio had never seen anything like it.
It was as if he wanted to punish himself for his irascible
conduct towards his wife and everybody. He invited the
whole of the English colony to the dinner. It was a classic
event that cost him five hundred pounds. The Italian nota-
bilities were also invited. A chef had been imported from the
Grand Hotel at Milan. The champagne flowed. There was
a dance band from Bologna. Eighty guests sat down to
dinner, one for each year of his life, as he remarked when
responding to the toast elegantly proposed by Guy Maysmith
and seconded by Hugh Trent. The Reverend Tobias
Smollett, in a purple waistcoat, said he would like to recite
a poem by Yeats that seemed appropriate to the occasion.
He declaimed the lines in his mellifluous voice:

> *When you are old and grey and full of sleep*
> *And nodding by the fire, take down this book*
> *And slowly read and dream of the soft look*
> *Your eyes had once and of their shadows deep.*
> *How many loved your moments of glad grace,*
> *And loved your beauty with love false or true,*
> *But one man loved the pilgrim soul in you*
> *And loved the sorrows of your changing face. . . .*

It was loudly applauded, the more so for the implied
compliment to Mary Crackenthorpe, gentle and lovely
beside the old man who had made life a trial for her.

In his response to the birthday toast Crackenthorpe took
their breath away. He owed his long and happy life, he said,
to the devotion of his dear wife. He had only one regret, that
he had not met her fifty years ago, and known even longer
happiness. This brought a sour smile to the face of Mrs.
Gavin, who was quick to point out to her neighbour that
fifty years ago Mary Crackenthorpe would have been
only sixteen—"But he always liked them young," she
added.

Crackenthorpe's speech was gallant. The tribute it contained to his wife's care of him drew warm applause. They accepted the *amende honorable*, but some remained sceptical. Could an old bear retract his claws? They would see. Father Crotti and Dr. Martini exchanged smiles. They hoped for the best. When the great cake came in, ablaze with eighty candles, a *tour-de-force* of the chef from the Grand Hotel, Henry Crackenthorpe brought down the house by taking a deep breath and extinguishing the quadruple rows of candles in one mighty blast. "The old chap'll make ninety," said Dr. Martini to Mrs. Viviani.

Martini's prophecy came true, though the good man did not live to see it. That autumn a maniac house-painter from Munich set the world in flames. The British colony was scattered. Some escaped to England, others were interned in a Tuscan hilltown, among them Crackenthorpe and his wife. Martini remained in Ligurio, a marked man because of his pro-British sympathies. He made gallant efforts to prevent the "devoted" Marias and Pietros from looting the villas in which they had served, now occupied by German officers. When the Teuton tide began to recede he joined the Partisans. Although over sixty he took to the mountains, was trapped and shot like a dog before the grave he was compelled to dig for himself. His companions in death were eighteen young Italians, all in their twenties.

When in 1946 the English colony came back they were a sadly reduced body; only one-quarter of the original members returned. Natural or violent deaths had winnowed them. Their fortunes were depleted by inflation, severe currency restrictions cut off any new recruits. The villas were dilapidated, looted of their furniture except for a few cases where the servants had remained to guard them, or had hidden away the carpets and silver.

The Crackenthorpes coming back from icy Certaldo, the home town of Boccaccio, whose house was bombed to rubble, found they had been lucky. Death had not caught them in

Certaldo, robbery had not denuded the Villa Escalonia. It had been occupied by a German general, who, quite assured that after Germany's victory he could permanently annex it, took great pains to keep it in perfect order. He employed four soldier-gardeners outside and three batmen inside. All these costless servants were placed under the control of Giuseppe and his wife Lucrezia, Crackenthorpe's faithful Italian retainers. The general, after the capitulation, left the villa, with tears in his eyes, robbed of a warm nest for his declining years. He wrote his unseen host a letter of thanks, expressing the hope that in happier times he might return as a guest.

When the Crackenthorpes returned they were eighty-seven and seventy-three respectively. Life in Ligurio was never the same again. The profiteers arrived from Milan, Turin, and Genoa and bought up the villas and their contents at knockdown prices. They were so frightened by the collapse of the lira to a twentieth of its former value that they rushed to put their paper money into bricks and mortar. The jerry builder came in to pluck them. Huge concrete skyscraper apartment houses reared their window-slotted heads along the blue Mediterranean shore from Ventimiglia to Genoa. These concrete honeycombs dried out and cracked in the sun. Perforated by icy blasts from the Ligurian alps in winter, roasted in summer, their inhabitants passed from the frigidaire to the hotplate. Elderly ladies thawing out in cafés baked in the noonday sun, crouched in the evening over ash-grey wood fires, blue-nosed in their woollens. Mrs. Smollett's chilblains defied all treatment. The organ practice for Sunday became an obstacle race over keys like blocks of ice. The price of coal defied the laws of gravity and rose and rose. Only the plutocrats, Sir Aubrey Wellington, the Contessa Verdecampo di Saluzzo, the Slocombes, and Sir John and Lady Crossley burnt anthracite in their boilers with the recklessness of South African mine millionaires. It was a nice problem whether it was cheaper to lose at cards all day in the

heated bridge club or burn olive-tree wood in the Franklin
stoves at home. The good bridge players had no problem
save the supply of victims.

The shopkeepers were puzzled by the change. What had
happened to the English who had been so remunerative for
eighty years or more? They now asked the price of everything, scrutinised their bills, questioned the weight and
quality, and altogether developed a mean exactitude. There
were stories of the Misses Simpson starving in the unpainted
Villa Richmond. They came no more to the Café Valentino
for their "elevenses"—always gin and vermouth with a
meringue. They accepted no invitations to cocktail parties
since they could not return them. They were touchily proud
and barred their bougainvillea-embowered garden door.
When Miss Matilda died a rumour spread that there was no
cash for the funeral. Sir Aubrey Wellington visited the Banca
Luzzati, that knew the skeleton in every *Inglese's* cupboard.
Signor Luzzati was glad to inform Miss Janet Simpson that
a client had paid an advance for her olive crop next autumn.
Miss Janet was grateful and surprised. Everyone prophesied
a miserable crop. Her own olive-groves were as unpromising
as all the others. The advance just covered the funeral
expenses. It was one more proof of her belief in the Lord's
bounty. The community sent so many wreaths that it was a
spectacular procession that moved from the English church
up to the cypress-shaded cemetery where the lower corner
was reserved for the Protestants who had ended their days
in Ligurio.

II

By 1947 there was a little recovery. Some of the villas
were reopened, a few new members, like Sir Aubrey Wellington and Contessa Verdecampo had joined the colony, having
resources outside the frozen pound. Miss Matilda Simpson,
forty years earlier the most formidable performer at the
English Tennis Club, and on one notable occasion the

partner of the great H. L. Doherty at a tournament held to raise funds for the new church, had only been buried a month, with the wreaths newly withered on her uncurbed grave, when the colony suffered a greater loss.

Mary Crackenthorpe died, as quietly and graciously as she had lived. One day she complained of feeling tired, went upstairs and was found dead on her bed when Lucrezia entered the room to turn down the covers. It was a thunderbolt for Henry Crackenthorpe. She was only seventy-four. He was eighty-eight, fourteen years her senior. It was unthinkable that she should go first. It was also inconsiderate, he felt. He was left to the mercy of Italian servants, lonely in a large villa. He wept copiously and was inconsolable. An angel on earth had gone to her rest, a little prematurely. In all his married life one thing had never occurred to him, that his wife might die first. He had never believed Dr. Martini's warning, and the nun who had seemed so young in 1915 with her rosy cheeks and lavender-blue eyes still seemed young to him. The shock sent him to bed for two days. He had to plead with the doctor to be allowed to attend the funeral. It was a very old man, the oldest in the community, that stood by the open grave and heard the earth rattle on the coffin as Father Crotti said the committal lines in the Catholic cemetery.

All Ligurio crowded the parish church and followed the hearse up to the cemetery. The Italians far outnumbered the English. The legend of her furtive benevolence, her response to all want and sickness in the houses of the fishermen, dark insanitary hovels under the ponderous arches of picturesque tenements, spread through the town and countryside. She was also a figure of romance. She had fled from a nunnery to embark on marriage at the age of forty-two. She had nursed the Italian wounded through the First Great War, and during the Second, at Certaldo, there was not a house with sickness in it where she had not ministered untiringly. Even when the natives, bombed by Allied planes, turned in fear and anger against the interned English, suspicious that by connivance they had drawn these deathly visitations in the sky, the calm face of the Signora helped to restrain them from any violence towards their involuntary guests. Her departure for Ligurio at the close of the war had evoked a demonstration of affection from the war-torn Certaldesi. And to this legend of her many virtues was added the crowning one. Despite her early error, she lived and died a good Catholic. Father Crotti, now the leading priest in the *parrocchia*, was seen to shed tears at the graveside.

Within a week two more blows fell upon Henry Crackenthorpe. He received news of the death of his brother Sherman. Their sister had died during the Second World War. This left him almost alone in the world. There was a great-nephew somewhere in Australia, unknown, unseen. His brother, he learned, had died in a Nottingham nursing home. His estate was worth about a quarter of a million pounds, the fruit of a long life of parsimony. The Government took more than half, the residue went to the unseen great-nephew. For this, Sherman Crackenthorpe had begrudged the cost of shoe-cleaning in hotels, and had lived in the gloom to save electricity bills. Henry took the news of his brother's death placidly. They had lived their lives apart for sixty years, and had rarely met or corresponded. They were antipathetic to each other.

The second blow Crackenthorpe did not take placidly. It stirred up the dormant fire of the volcano. Amazed, enraged, he shook with passion, a terrifying old man confronting the pallid Florentine lawyer who called upon him. It transpired that in her will, made thirty years earlier, Mrs. Crackenthorpe had left her property, the Villa Escalonia, to the Order of the Blue Sisters, together with two thousand pounds.

Giuseppe, the butler, hearing a terrific argument proceeding in the study, went and listened at the door, partly out of apprehension, partly out of curiosity. The old man might break a blood-vessel if he carried on like that. His employer was fluent in Italian, most fluent in the unprintable Italian he had learned among the estate workers of Ponte Arco. The lawyer, with a thinner, slower voice, tried to interpolate but was washed away in a torrent of denunciation.

"You can tell those Blue Sisters that not one of them shall set foot in this house, not if they come with the Pope and all the conclave of Cardinals. Here I've lived, and here I'll die! To hell with my wife's will! I'll bet they got her in a corner and frightened her into signing away the villa with threats of eternal damnation and all the rest of the claptrap they turn on terrified old women in their death-rattle. Go and tell that old Mother Superior and all her blue-black sisterhood, that I'll burn the villa down rather than be kicked out of my own home. Get out, you buzzing meat-fly. *Subitissimo!* Out! or for all my eighty-eight years I'll throw you out!"

The door suddenly opened, revealing the butler, mouth agape.

"Show this piece of parchment to the door!" cried Crackenthorpe, purple in the face, the black veins snaked on his temples.

"*Si, signore!*" said Giuseppe, startled.

The young lawyer picked up his attaché case and without a word followed the butler to the door.

III

All that day Henry Crackenthorpe was in a state of rage. He went into his wife's room and took away the roses he put in front of her portrait each morning. The hussy had tricked him after all. He had never suspected that she was capable of such deceit. He had loved her very dearly despite episodes that still rankled in his mind, his expulsion from her bedroom, her irritating humility, her supreme gift for always making him feel that he was in the wrong. Yet he loved her

and the last years together had passed in harmony. He medi-
tated on these. She had willed the villa away thirty years
ago, after she had made her peace with the Church, and
after they had gone through a second marriage in a Catholic
church to set her mind at rest. She had been warned that a
civil marriage with a Protestant could not be accepted by
the Church. She was living in a state of sin. They were
married very quietly in a Tyrolean village one summer's day.
The year of that marriage was the year of her will. As for the
five thousand pounds he had given her, she had been free to
do what she liked with it. Most of it had been given away in
her charitable acts. He did not begrudge the Blue Sisters a
penny of the two thousand pounds legacy. What hurt him
was that his wife should have slyly willed away the villa and
left him roofless.

He brooded in his chair all day. He would fight the will
whatever it cost. In Italy you could carry on a case for
twenty years. He would be dead before that, but he'd do it.
He would refuse to quit. He would die in possession of the
villa.

IV

The next morning after breakfast he began to read *The
Times*, a day old on its arrival in Ligurio, as was his custom.
It was a slow business, for his sight was failing badly and he
read laboriously with the aid of a powerful magnifying-glass.
He no longer read the obituary column for no one he knew
now appeared in it; they had all died.

He turned first to the financial page and looked at the
state of his stocks. He was comforted this morning by the
discovery that his Shell oil shares had risen one and sixpence,
and his Marks and Spencer Ltd. by half a crown. He picked
up a memo pad and made a calculation. He was one
thousand four hundred pounds better off this morning. He
lit one of his most expensive cigars and sat back in his winged
chair. What a pity he had not taken up another thousand

shares in that excellent oil company, a sure-growth stock. It did not occur to him to consider what possible benefit a sure-growth stock could be to a man of eighty-eight, worth two hundred thousand pounds, of which more than half would soon go to the British Government in death duties. His income was more than adequate, but the momentum of a lifetime of thrift still carried him in his habits. It had irritated him that Mary always cut away half an inch of cheese with the rind, and was extravagant with butter. Yet he subscribed generously and systematically to a good list of charities. The loss of the villa was only a matter of ten or twelve thousand pounds, the equivalent of a bonus issue he had had on his Burma oil holdings last year. It was the nature of the legacy and not the worth of it that outraged him. Mary had turned him into the street. He could not forgive such treachery reaching him from the grave.

His cigar finished, he rose to go out on the terrace to cut roses, but not for her portrait this morning. He began searching madly for the secateurs, buried in the chaos of his desk. He lost everything these days; there had been a frantic hunt, on rising, for his teeth, only to discover later, stamping about and fuming, that they were in his mouth.

The door opened during his feverish hunt for the secateurs. Giuseppe announced Signor Luzzati of the local bank. Crackenthorpe was surprised to see the banker, a long-sighted fellow who had most of Ligurio, mortgaged, in his hand. He was polite and obliging. Without him the English colony could hardly have survived. He cashed their cheques, arranged their purchases, tenancies, mortgages and "lets". He paid their taxes for them, versed in the intricacies of the Italian law which had a rubbery flexibility, following the Latin passion for "arrangements", the verb *arrangiare*—"to arrange" being much in use in the Italian world of affairs. Withal he was magnanimous. When old Mrs. Waring died penniless, he paid the nursing-home bill and the funeral expenses. To the English who continued to live for forty years in Ligurio without learning a hundred words of Italian he was invaluable. He could tell the plumber, the glazier, the gas-meter collector, the wood merchant, what was troubling the English occupant of the Villa Tutte. He could supply to the garage mechanic the Italian equivalent of "transmission", "back-axle", "oil sump" and "petrol-gauge". When Mrs. Viviani's husband swindled her and went off with a cinema usher he knew how to set the law in motion and recover her silver as her husband was about to board the *Conte Verde* for Buenos Aires.

There was nothing that defeated Signor Luzzati, a widower, except the sister who ran his home, a drill sergeant in black satin who recruited new servants every month. Endowed with the rare gift of secrecy, he had a hundred skeletons in his cupboards, deposited by British residents in Ligurio. Elderly and elegant, a product of Harrow and Trinity College, Cambridge, to which an English mother had insisted on his being sent, he sat in a small office behind the public one, brightened by the shining silver trophies he had won at tennis all over Europe in his youth. He never visited clients except by special request, and he carefully kept away from their cocktail parties, a reticence that gave him a judicial standing.

Crackenthorpe was astonished, therefore, when the butler announced Signor Luzzati, who came uninvited. He was wary at once. He was here on the Blue Sisters business obviously. When Luzzati had sat down at his invitation he tackled him at once.

"I know what you're here for!" he said gruffly, secateurs in hand, having just found them. "It's this Blue Sisters business. Well, Luzzati, take it from me they're not going to push me out! When they walk in here, if ever they do, it will be over my dead body."

"You are quite correct, Signor Crackenthorpe. It is the Blue Sisters business," said Luzzati, taking the cigar offered him. He lit it, carefully rolled it in his fingers, and then

slowly drew at it. He knew the high quality of old Crackenthorpe's best Havanas. Then he spoke again.

"Yesterday I was called on by Signor Pirelli, your wife's
Florentine lawyer. He told me that after informing you of
the contents of the will in which Mrs. Crackenthorpe left this
villa to the Blue Sisters, you were rather violent and said you
would contest the legacy. I gather the language you used
rather stunned the young man. It was his father who drew
up the will for Mrs. Crackenthorpe, when he was here in
Ligurio in 1917. He died later."

"One moment, before you go any further," interposed
Crackenthorpe, sitting on the edge of his leather chair,
secateurs still in hand. "If you come here, conniving with
that fellow, and thinking you're going to make me change
my mind, you're mistaken. Nothing will get me out of this
villa. I'll burn the damn' place before I'll go."

"That would be very costly, and could involve you in a
serious charge of arson," said Luzzati with a smile.

"Arson—hell!" shouted Crackenthorpe. "What's your
next move? Come on, out with it!"

"You must know that I would not advise anything against
your interest," said Luzzati, watching his smoke ascend.
"It is in your interest that I've called."

"Very good of you," retorted Crackenthorpe acidly.

"There's one point I should make before I go further,"
said Luzzati. "Has it occurred to you that your wife may
have made her legacy to the Blue Sisters for the same reason
that you got me to have this villa registered in her name—
that she quite reasonably assumed, as you did, that she'd
outlive you? Had you died before her this legacy would not
have been recalled to your memory."

"Recalled! I like that! This is the first I've ever heard
about it! I concede your point about my pre-deceasing her.
Still, she should have told me."

"It was unnecessary, since you knew," said Luzzati,
taking out his wallet.

"I tell you I never knew a thing about her intention! Do you imagine I'd let her give my home away, with me in it?" cried Crackenthorpe, putting down the secateurs with a bang. "The whole idea's preposterous, an absolute invention!"

"Mrs. Crackenthorpe's intention was to give the villa on her death to the Blue Sisters, as you could have no possible use for it, being in your grave. And to this you assented."

"I did nothing of the kind! When that fellow called yesterday it was the first time I'd heard of the legacy."

Luzzati opened his wallet, and extracted a sheet of paper which he unfolded.

"We are dealing with an act of thirty years ago and the memory being very fallible in the course of time, I have learnt never to trust to it wholly. When Signor Pirelli called on me after his stormy reception here, I recalled something. I took out your dossier and in it I found the following *aide-mémoire*. It is dated July 3rd, 1917, in my handwriting:

" 'Signor Pirelli, 1141 Via Malfi, Florence—discussed in presence of Mr. and Mrs. Crackenthorpe and self, draft of proposed will. The terms drawn. Villa Escalonia bequeathed to the Convent of B. Sisters, together with £2,000.'"

He passed the sheet of paper to Crackenthorpe.

"It's a sheer invention!" exclaimed the latter, taking it.

Luzzati broke the ash of his cigar into the tray, and looked steadily at the old man before him.

"My dear Mr. Crackenthorpe, you do not seriously suggest that I have just forged that *aide-mémoire*? For what purpose? If you will forgive me, old men forget. I had not forgotten this legacy, and happily I have this *aide-mémoire*.

On July 3rd, 1917, you and your wife, the late Enrico Pirelli, her attorney, and I, in my office, agreed on the draft of her will by which she gave the villa, and two thousand pounds to the Blue Sisters. Our error was that in 1917, you being fifty-eight and your wife forty-four, none of us had the wits to foresee the improbable possibility—that she might die first. What was done was done with your knowledge—but you have forgotten."

Crackenthorpe sat quietly in his chair, his veined hands restless on its arms, his face trembling with emotion. The fire had gone out of him, he sat there an abject figure of age.

"Old men forget," he repeated in a flat voice. "Old men forget—I suppose I'm ga-ga. That's it, ga-ga!"

"You are a very remarkable man for your age."

"I'm a very remarkable old fool! Well, what do I do now, get out, or try to buy back the place?"

"Neither. You didn't give that poor young lawyer an opportunity to open his mouth," said Luzzati.

"I was up to my old form. I ordered him out of the house," agreed Crackenthorpe with a grim smile.

"What he intended telling you, had you given him the opportunity, is that the Mother Superior has no intention of taking over the villa until after your death."

"Much obliged to her, but I may make a hundred."

"I'm sure she hopes you will—and should you need it, she might send a sister to nurse you," added Luzzati, rising, with a chuckle.

Crackenthorpe looked down at his hands on the chair. Then he said slowly, as he got up to accompany Luzzati into the hall, "Over thirty years ago I was nursed by a Blue Sister who dropped her tears on my hand, she was so sorry for me. She was the angel who married an old devil. There could never be another Blue Sister like that."

When Luzzati had gone, Crackenthorpe picked up the secateurs and went out on the terrace where he cut half a dozen of the most beautiful roses. It was early June and they were in their glory. He carried them indoors and put them in a vase, placing it, as formerly, under his wife's portrait in the morning-room.

"Old men forget. Forgive me, Mary," he said to the woman smiling down at him.

V

It looked as if he would make a hundred. His ninetieth birthday came and was quietly celebrated. But he grew increasingly testy and difficult. One March day, in his ninety-second year, he walked down into the town, had himself measured for half a dozen shirts and came back in an open carriage singing hilariously, but not quite drunk. He caught a chill and was put to bed with a temperature, but the next Sunday he was at church, in his customary place. He was startled to hear Smollett embark on *The Song of Solomon*.

He listened, a little derisively, but towards the end of the lesson his mind wandered.

Make haste, my beloved, and be thou like to a roe or to a young hart upon the mountain of spices.

He had once been a not-so-young hart upon the mountain of spices. How long ago? Longer than anyone here could remember, or cared to remember.

When he got back to the Villa Escalonia he went to his study and got out the Bible. He wanted to read *The Song of Solomon* for himself. It had brought back happy memories.

He sat down, opened the Bible, and with his magnifying-glass slowly read the lyrical verses.

Many waters cannot quench love, neither can the floods drown it. If a man would give all the substance of his house for love, he would be utterly contemned.

The gong rang for lunch. Giuseppe waited a few minutes. The *signore* not coming, he went to the study. There he found him, his head resting on the Bible, magnifying-glass in hand, his eyes and ears for ever closed to *The Song of Solomon*.

CHAPTER I

IN the gospel according to Mrs. Gavin, a compilation of myth and malice based on inadequate facts, there was something "mysterious" about Mrs. Callender. She went nowhere, she knew no one, she had no relations. "And from her conversation, which consists of monosyllables dragged out of her, she seems to have had no past!" complained Mrs. Gavin. "Who was Mr. Callender—I suppose he did exist?"

"He was a very good-looking young man. I've seen his portrait. They had not been married long when she lost him. Poor Mrs. Callender never recovered from the shock," said Mrs. Smollett.

"How ridiculous!" retorted Mrs. Gavin. "The profession of widow died out with Queen Victoria! There's something wrong with a pretty young woman—and she must have been very pretty forty years ago—who doesn't re-marry. I re-married within two years of Frank's death. I was twenty-eight, and I loved my second husband more than my first."

Mrs. Callender was mysterious. She lived in a small villa just above the church, which she had rented and then bought. When she arrived in 1946 she knew no one. Twice a week she appeared at the English library to change her books; once a week, on Sunday morning, she went to the English church. Her first callers were the Reverend and Mrs. Smollett. On their favourable report, Lady Crossley and the Contessa Verdecampo di Saluzzo left cards. Mrs. Callender was socially launched in Ligurio, but she took very little advantage of this. She rarely went out, she rarely entertained. It was understood that her means were "very restricted" in the polite parlance of Ligurio. It was more bluntly put by Mrs. Gavin. "She hasn't a penny to her name, and scarcely a rag to her back—so I'm not taken in by her aristocratic reticence!"

Mary Callender had an aristocratic reticence. She wore her few clothes with an air, her manners were exquisite. When she spoke her voice was modulated and pleasing. She rarely smiled, but when she did so her beautiful blue eyes had a singular light. There rested upon her a suggestion of some distant tragedy in her life. The only clue to this was that one day she remarked that her young husband had died suddenly. What that end was no one knew, and it would not have been seemly to have pressed gentle Mrs. Callender for facts that she found too painful to divulge. She lived in and moved about Ligurio always a little withdrawn from the restricted and intimate English circle.

On the Sunday morning that the Reverend Tobias Smollett blundered into the reading of *The Song of Solomon*, she did not stay for Holy Communion, as was her custom. A close observer would have seen that she was perturbed by something. After the service she hurried away, avoiding the customary groupings and gossip in the pleasant garden of the church where the worshippers lingered in the warm sunshine of the Italian noon. She mounted the steps of the cobbled path that wound up through the olive-groves to the small plateau on which stood the Villa Chiara, her home. It had two gables, with a ground and upper floor. The six windows, with green shutters, commanded a magnificent view of the crescent bay, with the grey and red tiles of the town like a mottled carpet covering the half-moon plain below. The villa had a long garden in two terraces, with six tall cypress trees that gave the scene a dramatic character. It was entirely walled in and no one could gain access except by ringing the bell at the outer gate. This was seldom answered since Mrs. Callender employed a stone-deaf maid. Her self-willed isolation was complete. No one knew what she did with her time except reading and gardening. She rarely went out. Unlike most of the colony she remained in her villa throughout the year and never made the customary summer migration to England.

On her return to the Villa Chiara from the church service Mrs. Callender went straight up the small marble staircase to her bedroom. Closing the door, she took off her hat and put it on the mirror-dressing table before which she sat. She observed herself in the mirror as if searching for something in the calm expression of her face. At seventy her skin was still fresh and lightly lined. She used no make-up, for her natural colouring was good, even her lips retained the moist crimson of youth. She could not be called a good-looking old lady, for there was nothing old in her appearance or manner, save the gravity of her disposition. Her hair, silver white, was abundant, her figure slim. Mrs. Gavin's speculation on a long unnecessary widowhood was not without foundation. She had been a beautiful woman these last fifty years.

Mrs. Callender, after removing her hat and resting her hands on the dressing-table, made no movement. Outwardly she seemed a woman in complete repose. Inwardly her mind was in a state of tumult. The words of *The Song of Solomon* rang through her brain. *Many waters cannot quench love, neither can the floods drown it.* How very true they were, how poignantly true!

Presently she rose and stood looking out of the french window that opened on to the balcony. All Ligurio lay in sunshine below her. The golden mimosa, the roses of the pergola and the pink peach blossom bloomed in the villa's terraces under the deep blue sky. The bay sparkled as a solitary ship, a liner, passed swiftly along the chord of the bay, possibly on its passage to Marseilles and New York. Once, long ago, she had contemplated beginning a new life in the New World. Now she knew she would never make that passage, having found here in Ligurio a haven until her death.

She watched the liner till it disappeared beyond the headland, then she turned from the window and crossed the cosily furnished bedroom that served also as boudoir and study to the small Sheraton bedside-table with its parchment-shaded reading-lamp. From a drawer she took out a leather case, unfastened the brass clasp, and opened it. The small double frames held two portraits. She raised these to her lips, kissed them, and after a few moments of contemplation, closed the case and replaced it in the drawer.

Many waters cannot quench love, neither can the floods drown it. The lines of the morning's First Lesson rang in her head. She lay down on the chaise-longue and closed her eyes in the quiet room. There was half an hour to lunch. A youth, probably Mario, the gardener's son in the adjacent villa, was singing an aria from *Madam Butterfly*, in the sob-laden voice with which the Italians exult in melodious misery.

Mrs. Callender lay quite still, but her mind travelled far down through the years, to a dahabeeyah on the Nile, to a house in Queen's Gate, London, to a street in Madrid, to an assize court in Oxford. She lay there in the silent house, the whole panorama of her life revolving before her closed eyes, brought out of the past by the Reverend Tobias Smollett and King Solomon.

CHAPTER II

I

A FRENCH marquis of notorious reputation had built the Villa Bonjour on the outskirts of Luxor. He had been a pioneer before the days when Egypt had been made a fashionable resort by the novels of Robert Hichens, who later lived in one of the adjacent villas with a garden that went down to the Nile. In the year 1900 the English occupied Egypt, optimistic that under their tutelage the land of the Pharaohs could be disciplined into law, order and honesty. The tomb of Tutankhamen lay unknown beneath a mountain of debris in the Valley of the Tombs of the Kings, the great hotels, embowered in bougainvillea and giant palms, had just arisen to house the wealthy refugees from Europe's winter, and a steady service of luxurious steamboats ascended the Nile from Cairo to the great dam being built at Aswan. After a halt at Luxor they passed the walled garden of the Villa Bonjour, ascending to the First Cataract, on a course dotted with the dahabeeyahs that housed the wealthy Europeans and Egyptians who took their pleasure in the fabulous land of the vanished Pharaohs.

The quarterings in the arms of the Marquis Henri Hyacinthe Latour de Villefranche proved his unimpeachably aristocratic descent. Unfortunately they could not prove the unimpeachable character of their possessor. On the contrary, they attracted a rather embarrassing attention. A line that had sent counts to the Crusades, recruited Priors for the chivalrous Order of the Knights of Rhodes, married into the ducal houses of Luynes, Montmorency, La Rochefoucauld and Richelieu, had come to a bizarre end in the eccentric Marquis Henri Latour de Villefranche. His father's marriage with the daughter of a Cuban sugar magnate had provided him with a disastrous fortune. He led a vivid life of disreputable activity in various parts of the world. By the age of forty he had sampled the unsavoury aspects of life in Paris, Rio de Janeiro, New Orleans, Berlin, Rome, Algiers, Vienna and Athens. In all of these places there had been "incidents" that had resulted in police enquiries. His last refuge had been Cairo, where his peculiar tastes excited no attention.

At the turn of the century the marquis built a villa on the banks of the Nile at Luxor. He furnished it with an exotic extravagance and over its staff placed the smiling Lo Chen, his Chinese butler, conversant with every form of vice practised from Shanghai to Bombay. The most remarkable thing about the marquis was not his singular tastes but his considerable stamina. No excesses tired him. Debonair, handsome, a poet, bird fancier, spiritualist, an authority on the English dramatists of the Restoration, author of a monograph on Baudelaire, founder and proprietor of a private factory for ceramics, donor of the *Codex Mauritius* to the Bibliothèque Nationale, a one-time captain in the Vatican Swiss Guard, donor to the French Archæological Mission in Leptis Magna, whose *Transactions* he edited and printed, bound in vellum, at his château at La Roche Rennil—his infinite variety had been extended to the field of matrimony. He had married, first, Donna Faviola, daughter of Prince Cesare Nagaroli-Landini, by whom he came into possession of a fourteenth-century castle at Cestona in the Val d'Aosta. His wife ran away with a Spanish matador whom he had kept for two years. The matador proved more expensive and unpredictable than the horse Henri entered for the Grand National at Aintree. It was a triple achievement for him to have lost in one year his wife, the matador and the Grand National.

His second marriage was a matter of spite. He detested his cousin and heir, Robert Coulaindot, a serious young man with Trappist tendencies, who spent his time going into seclusion in various monasteries. The thought of him sitting

in the great salon at La Roche Rennil, with half a dozen
black-frocked priests debating the pros and cons of papal
recognition of the Assumption of the Virgin Mary, drove
Henri into a second experiment in matrimony. The first
marriage failing to deprive the sanctimonious Robert of the
succession, he chose Nadia, the buxom daughter of the Grand
Duke Alexis Romanoff. Five of her married sisters had produced eleven boys, a male predominance that augured well
for Henri. The result was nil. After five futile years there was
an annulment. Nadia married again, and within a year
produced twin boys. Henri never quite recovered from this
implied impotence. Two years later, in 1900, he was found
doped and smothered in his dahabeeyah moored off the
Villa Bonjour. A Nubian boatboy, charged with the murder,
was acquitted.

The finale had a surprising sequel. His alienable estate
was willed to found a boys' orphanage. It was stipulated that
the boys should wear blue shorts with yellow stockings, and
blue berets. The colours were those of the Latour de Villefranche livery. Cousin Robert succeeded to the marquisate,
to three châteaux and two estates. Ironically, a Jesuit friend
was appointed to administer the orphanage.

On inheriting the Villa Bonjour the new marquis had the
pornographic frescoes by the great Russian painter Rousoff
effaced in the bathroom, and the villa exorcised by his
private chaplain. The villa and the dahabeeyah, *Cherami*,
with furnishings, were put on the market. An Englishman,
Hamilton Bostowell, with banking interests in Egypt and
England, bought the villa and the boat. He was a widower
with a son of eight at Summerfields School and a daughter
of twenty just out of Roedean.

Hamilton Bostowell was a big breezy man with a zest for
living. He spent freely and maintained three establishments,
a shoot at Largs in Scotland, a house in Queen's Gate,
London, and the Villa Bonjour at Luxor. He made the Hotel
Crillon his *pied-à-terre* when in Paris. His banking interests

caused him to be an incessant traveller in Europe. At the end
of the century his interests in the financing of the great new
dam at Aswan took him frequently to Egypt. He bought the
Villa Bonjour at Luxor as a half-way house between Cairo
and Aswan, making the trip, if time allowed, between Luxor
and Aswan, in his dahabeeyah, with a crew of ten super-
vised by an Omran Arab, Abu Omar.

II

Soon after his acquisition of the Villa Bonjour, Bostowell
took there his pretty young daughter, chaperoned by his
widowed sister, Mrs. Cavan. It was an exhilarating experience for a girl just out of school. Mary Bostowell created a
sensation on her arrival in Cairo. With her long golden hair,
her limpid blue eyes, high colouring and her beautiful figure,
she was the English rose in perfection. With these assets she
combined a vivacious spirit that soon gave her pre-eminence
among the girls of the English colony. A coming-of-age ball
was given for her at the Residency, with all the splendour of
the official ceremonial placed at her disposal by the Consul-
General, Lord Cromer. She was the toast of the mess in the
Cairo garrison, and her suitors, since competition was small
in this torrid outpost of England, consisted of every eligible
young officer. It was Cyril Ransome, on the staff of the
Consul-General, who led the runners. The heir to the peerage
of Drage, twenty-four, handsome, he found immediate
favour in the eyes of Hamilton Bostowell as well as of Mary.
The family was large and impoverished, but of ancient
lineage. The two young people shared a passion for riding
and tennis. If only her father had bought a house in Cairo
instead of a villa at Luxor, a twenty-hour overnight journey!

There were two Egyptian rivals. They had considerable
assets, personal and material. Young Prince Salah Nassif, of
a cadet-branch of the Khedieval family, had the brilliant
eyes of his Persian mother combined with the flashing

vivacity and dark colouring of his father. Educated at Harrow and Trinity, he possessed great personal charm. His fortune was modest, as Egyptian fortunes go, but his birth placed him apart. He was twenty-two and it was said that a marriage had already been arranged by his father. Nevertheless, he was assiduous in his attention to the English girl who had captivated Cairo.

His rival was a countryman of lower birth, but the heir to a vast fortune, the nephew of a half-Syrian, half-Egyptian Alexandria cotton magnate. Mohamed Kafi was that singular person in Egypt, a bachelor of thirty. He had a large estate in the Fayoum, a villa at Monte Carlo, a racing stable at Longchamps and one of the most sumptuous dahabeeyahs on the Nile, *The Lotus*. His racing colours were well known at Longchamps, and he was a passionate convert to the new sport of motoring. He was an intrepid driver with a charmed life. Reputed to be anti-English, he moved, nevertheless, in English as well as Egyptian circles.

His attentions to Mary Bostowell were embarrassing. He showered upon her flowers and boxes of bonbons, he sent round with one of his Circassian grooms the most beautiful horses from his stable outside Cairo for her to ride. Mary's aunt, Helen Cavan, tried to check these favours, but Kafi seeped in like a flood at all openings. Again and again she rebuffed the suave, smiling Egyptian, by making Mary decline his many invitations. She had been warned by members of the English colony that Kafi had an unsavoury reputation. Mr. Bostowell took his sister's warning very lightly. "Every Egyptian is alleged to have a harem of houris," he said. "I find Kafi very agreeable. I find Prince Salah a colourless bore. Anyhow, why worry? Mary seems taken by young Cyril Ransome. I only want her to have a good time—and not commit herself too soon."

Bostowell was never in any one place for long. He came fitfully to the Villa Bonjour. He had closed up the house in Queen's Gate. His life was absorbed in endless financial conferences that caused him to migrate between London, Paris and Cairo. He scarcely ever used the dahabeeyah moored off the villa. In December 1901, following his daughter's début, he had a house party at the Villa Bonjour. After visits to the Valley of the Kings and ancient Karnak, he transported his guests up the Nile to Aswan, where the dahabeeyah was moored off Elephant Island. The party consisted of a French banker and his wife, a saturnine Armenian reputed to be a multi-millionaire with vast oil interests, and two American business men and their wives, directors of a steel company for which Bostowell was arranging a debenture flotation. They were a grim group; finance, whisky and bridge absorbed their time.

One morning Bostowell took his party ashore to see the ancient quarries of Syene from which the obelisks had been extracted. His guests were more derisive than impressed. "They took ten years to hack out an obelisk! We've pneumatic rock drills that could do it in a week!" commented Hoover Gould.

When the dragoman pointed out that it had taken a month, and four hundred slaves, to move an obelisk on rollers from the quarry down to the Nile barge for water transport to Memphis, Chester Wainwright contemptuously threw away a chewed cigar, remarking: "If we'd been in business in the time of the Pharaohs we'd have shifted all his obelisks in two hours with a Wainwright Cantilever Truck, and have put up a pyramid in a month."

"If you'd been in business in Pharaoh's time and had built him a pyramid, you'd have been sealed up inside it to stop you doing it for another fellow," observed Mr. Moulmedji. "They liked to keep the copyright of all their constructions."

"They were a strange people," said Mrs. Hoover Gould. "Is it true that the Pharaohs really married their sisters? It sounds too degenerate!"

"I assure you, Mrs. Gould, despite the Mendelian theory,

that marriage between the Pharaohs and their sisters by no means impaired either their mental or their procreative powers," said Moulmedji. "No one ever suggested that Cleopatra, the product of such a union, was lacking in either pride or vivacity. It is true she objected to marrying her brother Ptolemy, as arranged, but that was because he wasn't willing to share the throne with her. So she picked up Julius Cæsar on his arrival in Egypt when pursuing Pompey. She diverted him into finishing off her elder brother, got herself made Queen by Cæsar, and then married her younger brother. She left him later to go off to Rome with Cæsar, to whom she bore a son. When Cæsar was murdered she took up with Mark Antony, as the world knows, to whom she bore two sons. Her choice was unfortunate. They fooled their time away in Alexandria, until the battle of Actium finished him. He fell on his sword and she chose an asp. The oddest thing of all was that Octavia—Antony's deserted wife—brought up Cleopatra's two boys by Antony. With that record no one could say Cleopatra, whose parents were brother and sister, lacked virility!"

"I could listen to you all day," cried Mrs. Hoover Gould. "You make history so human!"

"I think it's all dreadfully immoral. What becomes of the sanctity of marriage?" asked Mrs. Chester Wainwright.

"They were a rum lot, and they still are," observed Chester Wainwright, lighting another cigar.

Bostowell made no comment. He knew that Mrs. Wainwright had been through the divorce court three times, and at forty-eight Wainwright was her fourth experiment. The tangle of seven children from three marriages possibly provoked Mr. Moulmedji's quiet comment.

"The Pharaonic marriage system had the virtue of simplifying the line of succession. Many of the great wars of history, and, in modern times, of the great law cases, have devolved from a varied progeny contending with each other."

"Well I'm damned!" exclaimed Wainwright, searching the shore line with his binoculars. "Those fellahins are bathing stark naked! They're just a lot of rabbits, breeding and popping out of holes."

He put down his glasses with an air of disgust.

Mr. Moulmedji smiled in his deprecatory manner.

"There's a strong supposition that the glory that was Greece was derived from this land of the fellahin. Herodotus, who travelled here extensively, recorded that——"

"You talk like a professor!" exclaimed Hoover Gould, who said little and drank hard. "Whatever was derived from them, they stank then and they stink now!"

A Nubian servant appeared from below, banging a gong, announcing lunch. A white launch drew up silently alongside the *Cherami*. In it stood Mrs. Cavan, Mary, and its owner, Mohamed Kafi—immaculately dressed in white with curled black head, a dark Antinous of the Egyptian scene. They had just returned from an excursion to the island of Philæ and its ancient temple, soon to be buried by the raising of the water-level behind the Aswan dam. The archæological world was in uproar over the drowning of this "pearl of Egypt". For eight months of the year most of the beautiful temple of Isis, cherished by the ancient Egyptians, and later by the Roman emperors, Tiberius, Hadrian and Marcus Aurelius, would be submerged in the lake created by the new dam. Mrs. Cavan and Mary returned strong anti-dammers, horrified at the vandalism in the name of progress.

The party came aboard and Mohamed Kafi dispensed his charm among the ladies, all unaware of the disparaging comments of Hoover Gould that had preceded his advent. In half an hour, seated beside Mrs. Wainwright at the long lunch table under the green awning aft, he had so charmed his partner that he had engaged her and her husband to make a desert excursion by camel on the morrow.

"Alas, dear lady, we must start at seven o'clock; my

launch will take us to Meji, and there we will set out for the
Roman quarries."

"I think I've seen enough quarries!" protested Wainwright.

"But, Chester dear, these are very historical quarries.
They're where the ancient Romans got their porphyry from!
Of course we'll go. Mr. Kafi is just too kind!" asserted Mrs.
Wainwright.

What a fascinating man, what teeth, what really beautiful
brown hands her neighbour had! She glanced at them as he
played with the stem of his wineglass. She imagined them
framing her face while his dark eyes smiled at her. How
lovely her host's daughter was! To be twenty-one and not a
disguised forty-eight, and to have all these ravishing dark
young men dancing attendance. But the girl would have to
be careful. They were slick seducers. If Mrs. Cavan did not
watch out there might be a disaster. Young girls could not
possibly know how to play with Egyptian fire. Widely experienced, there was no fire she could not play with,
reflected Mrs. Wainwright, but of late the flames had not
burned so fiercely at her approach. Now, she smiled on Kafi
Effendi, the sense of romance stirred in her, for he had an
alluring way of looking at one.

"I believe the great porphyry basin in the rotunda of the
Vatican Galleries was derived from those quarries. It's said
to be the largest porphyry basin in the world and once stood
in the Baths of Diocletian," said Mr. Moulmedji softly,
smiling at Mrs. Wainwright.

"Say, is there anything you don't know?" asked Hoover
Gould, a little irritably.

"A great deal, my dear Mr. Gould. I do not know the
current prices of many stocks on the New York Stock
Exchange, in which you are deeply versed, I am told. My
particular field is Arabian oil, and even there I have many
lacunæ."

Moulmedji raised his glass in tribute to Hoover Gould, a
large diamond sparkling on his little finger.

"What are lacunæ? I'd love to see them!" exclaimed Mrs. Gould, insatiable for experiences of any kind.

"They are, alas, dear lady, only mentally visible. They are the regrettable blanks in my knowledge," explained Mr. Moulmedji suavely.

"Moulmedji, you won't get away with that!" said Bostowell from the head of the table. "At five o'clock I've got a snake-charmer coming on board. I'll guarantee you could handle his stock!"

Mr. Moulmedji smiled. "Perhaps, perhaps, my dear friend. I have had some experience of snakes of various kinds." He turned to Hoover Gould. "Speaking of snakes, I would like your opinion on Anaconda Copper. I'm trustee of an estate in liquidation with a large holding in that company."

"Hang on to 'em," said Gould, curtly. He never knew whether the damned Armenian was serious or leg-pulling. He didn't like the snake reference, it sounded two-edged. When it came to anything slippery he'd back an Armenian every time. Moulmedji was renowned as an oily fellow in the oil world. Why was Bostowell so attentive to him? Something was brewing.

"Tomorrow I shall have the pleasure of presenting Mary with the camel that she will ride on," murmured Mohamed Kafi in his musical voice. "She is a very gentle creature, and still has three teeth."

"Oh, Mohamed, how exciting. Do you really mean it?" cried Mary, her eyes sparkling with anticipation.

Bostowell gave a look at his sister. He was doubly startled. Since when had it reached a Mary and Mohamed basis, and why had his sister let the affair develop as far as a camel present? And what a present!

"My dear Mohamed Kafi—it is most kind of you. But what on earth would Mary do with a camel when we go back to London next spring?" asked Bostowell.

"That is most simple," responded Kafi imperturbably, his

glittering smile embracing the company. "Mimi—that is her name, after *Bohème*, for, being a young camel, she is very consumptive"—he paused for a laugh at the pun, which failed to come—"Mimi will go back to my stables until Mary returns, which we all hope will be very soon."

"If it is a young camel, why has it only three teeth left?" asked Hoover Gould.

"Are they coming or going?" asked Wainwright, provoking a laugh.

A slight shade of annoyance swept over the Egyptian's smiling face.

"I should explain that only young camels have three teeth. When they reach maturity only one tooth, the third, remains," said Kafi.

"I assume it is a camel *dromedarius* and not *bactrianus*?" asked Moulmedji.

"What's the difference?" asked Wainwright, peeling an orange.

"It's a camel that has one hump, a bactrian camel has two," explained Kafi.

"Then my second husband was a bactrian—unless there's another kind of camel with ten humps," interjected Mrs. Wainwright airily. All the table laughed.

"Miss Mary, and you, my dear Bostowell, need have no apprehension about keeping a camel," said Moulmedji. "It's a most profitable animal, dead or alive. It supplies everything but gallantry and affection. It will bite its best friend and when victorious in a fight it will stamp its adversary to death! Camel fights are more degrading spectacles than bullfights."

"I like a good bullfight!" interjected Hoover Gould.

"The camel, Miss Mary," continued Moulmedji, addressing her with his imperturbable mien and soft voice, "is a most rewarding animal, temper apart. It serves, alive, for transport and transit. Its milk makes butter and cheese, its hair, woven, makes admirable fabrics—such as this"—he touched his fawn cardigan lightly—"its dung serves as a fuel for Arabs, and from the soot of it they derive sal-ammoniac. Dead, the tanned skin is excellent for saddles and shoes. What animal could do more for one?"

Moulmedji raised his thin hands enquiringly.

"Have you ever eaten camel?" asked Hoover Gould, with a suggestion of cannibalism in the tone of his voice.

"Certainly. Once on an expedition with Mohamed Hassan Bey, in a quest for The Lost Oases, our transport was lost and we were compelled to kill a camel for its water and meat," replied Moulmedji.

"You drank its water!" exclaimed Gould, disgust in his voice.

Moulmedji smiled gently at the American.

"Compulsion doesn't wait on the connoisseur," he replied.

"And what's the meat like?" asked Mrs. Wainwright.

"The water was bitter, the meat rather sweet," answered Moulmedji. "Anyhow, I hope, Miss Mary, that will never be the end of your camel."

At a glance from Bostowell Mrs. Cavan gave the sign for the ladies to rise. The men lingered over coffee and liqueurs. Presently Wainwright got up. "I'm going to hit the mattress, see you later," he said.

"Don't forget the snake-charmer at five. I hear he's remarkable," called Bostowell to his departing guest.

Moulmedji lingered for a moment before joining the ladies. He surveyed the long flat palm-fringed bank of the Nile. He drew gently on his cheroot. He knew what was afoot with his host and those Americans. When it came to snake-charming he could put them all in the basket.

CHAPTER III

I

THE *Cherami* returned to its mooring opposite the Villa Bonjour late in January. Business drew Bostowell north to Cairo, where Mary and Mrs. Cavan joined him. They stayed out at the Mena House Hotel, their rooms looking on to the Great Pyramid. In February Cyril Ransome, tied by his duties at the Residency, was disconcerted by the increasing attentions paid by Prince Salah Nassif to Mary Bostowell. They rode together every day, they played tennis, they studiously visited the mosques and museums. Irritated, young Ransome lost his temper one day and referred disparagingly to the Prince. Mary retorted sharply and for a month they were scarcely on speaking terms. Then Mohamed Kafi came back from Paris, and Prince Salah had a serious rival. He took the Bostowells on a visit to his estate in the Fayoum, where Hamilton Bostowell enjoyed the excellent shooting. He saw a good example of the fabulous style in which rich Egyptians lived.

There was now some kind of business relationship between Bostowell and Kafi. The conferences in Cairo were frequent, with Moulmedji and Hoover Gould in the background.

Bostowell did not seem at all concerned by the news of the quarrel between his daughter and young Ransome. The growing resentment of the young English officers and officials at Kafi's monopoly of Mary seemed to pass unnoticed. Finally Mrs. Cavan sounded the alarm. "There is too much talk," she said to her brother. "I feel we should go back to Luxor."

"Very well—I can't come for the next three weeks," he said. "After that we'll leave for London."

There was a protest from Mary on hearing they were to go

to Luxor, but Bostowell was firm. "I don't want any trouble
with Kafi—he can be very useful to me, but I can quite
understand young Ransome's resentment. So I think you'd
better go to the villa for a time."

"I'm very fond of Cyril—but I'm not anybody's property
yet!" protested Mary hotly.

"Well, apply that admirable axiom to Kafi and Salah.
You're a mere girl. Soon we'll be back in England. You'll
have plenty of beaux there. Cyril's a nice lad, of a good
family. One day he'll be an ambassador. Cromer thinks
highly of him. So be nice to him. Also, I don't want any
situation to develop where I have to put my foot down with
Kafi. These Egyptians are troublesome gentry."

Admonished, Mary departed with Aunt Helen for Luxor.
They had been a week at the Villa Bonjour when Abu Omar
observed the Kafi dahabeeyah, the *Lotus*, moored by the
Winter Palace landing. He reported the matter at once to
Mrs. Cavan, as part of the casual news of the place. She
was not surprised therefore when the next day a Nubian
boatboy came with a note from Mohamed Kafi inviting Mrs.
Cavan and her niece to dinner, which he was giving for some
English and American friends on board the *Lotus*, and at which
his mother, who was staying at the Winter Palace Hotel, would
be present. He wished Mrs. Cavan and Mary to meet her.

The news that Kafi had a mother came as a surprise to
Mrs. Cavan. It was the first time she had heard of her. Yet
it was reasonable for Kafi, a man of thirty, to have a mother,
probably a widow living in retirement.

Mrs. Cavan hesitated before speaking to Mary, who had
already made allusions to her "exile". She could sympathise
with her niece. All the young people were in Cairo. Luxor
was a winter retreat for the elderly English and Americans.
The place was dead after dinner. Her brother had made it
clear that he desired no offence to be given to Kafi. He
would be here in a week and could deal with the situation
himself. She had felt somewhat alarmed when Abu Omar

announced the arrival of the *Lotus*. Now it seemed quite natural with Kafi's mother staying in Luxor.

When Mrs. Cavan spoke to Mary that evening, showing her the invitation, she asked, as unconcernedly as possible, whether they should accept. She was relieved by Mary's reply.

"Only if you would like to go, Auntie. I've met Madame Kafi in Cairo, at a charity bazaar. She's a very distinguished old lady, you would like her. But I hope Father won't think Mohamed's rushed here because of me. After all, the Nile does belong to the Egyptians!"

"That's been a fact for ten thousand years," commented Mrs. Cavan dryly. "Very well, we'll accept. But we'll go in our own launch, otherwise you never know when you can get away. These Egyptians have no sense of time."

The night of the party was that of the full moon. The Nile was a silver mirror, with the great wall of the rocks in the Valley of the Tombs of the Kings grey and monolithic in the moonlight. The *Lotus* was outlined by small coloured lanterns. A string orchestra was playing as they drew to her side. The crew in white liveries with gold facings and crimson sashes waited by the gangway. Hassan, the huge Sudanese dragoman, was resplendent in a crimson djelabieh and yellow turban.

There were about fifty guests present, of whom about half danced on the foredeck. A special dance band had been transported from Cairo, four hundred miles away. The dinner party preceding the dance was for twenty guests only. The Egyptians were in a minority, English and Americans visiting Luxor predominating. Madame Kafi was a little old lady of great dignity. She was a Syrian by birth and since her English was poor she spoke mostly in French. At a glance Mrs. Cavan appraised her jewellery at about fifty thousand pounds.

The scene was enchanting. In the warm night the Nile lay like a mirror under the moon. The east shore, with its hotels, sparkled with lights beyond the border of date palms.

On the west bank lay the plain, ending in the valley and the precipitous rock wall behind the Temple of Dar-el-Bahri, Queen Hatshepsut's tribute to Amon. Mary knew well this vast necropolis of the dead, with its sinister sun-baked ravines, its elaborate tombs of Pharaoh on Pharaoh, the vast Ramesseum, with its great pylons and towers faced with hieroglyphs proclaiming the conquest of the mighty Rameses II in his Syrian campaigns against the Hittites. She had stood beneath the towering colossus of Rameses in the first court. Through the second, colonnaded, she had passed to the massive Hypostyle Hall, a symbol of lost power and magnificence. Tomb on tomb, ravine on ravine, mighty ruin after ruin, all silent, all broken, desolate, sun-scorched, devised on a scale for giants to emphasise the brief earthly transit of man, bequeathed a few seconds of endeavour in the immeasurable calendar of Time.

Mary Bostowell had been singularly fortunate in the manner of her visit. She had no parrot-dialogued dragoman repeating his inaccurate fables, uninterruptable, nigh unintelligible with his peasant's French and English. At her side, day after day, Mohamed Kafi had been her illuminating guide. She felt dazed by his scholarship. He could interpret with great lucidity the hieroglyphs on the walls and tombs. The coloured reliefs lining the endless chambers of the dead were for him a simple picture-book. Under his clear elucidation, all Egypt marched in its stupendous pageantry down through the dynasties.

In one of the tombs, poorly lit by a single electric bulb on a long wire, they found a young French artist lying on his back on a plank, patiently copying a duck-shooting scene in the Fayoum. The Pharaoh and his attendants were enjoying a day's sport around 1500 B.C. An unknown artist of their day had drawn an exquisite panel of ducks in flight, one bird stricken and tumbling to its death.

The young Frenchman in this dark tomb chatted with them. He was copying the ducks for a frieze he was designing for a Paris night club. "Quelle délicatesse incroyable!" he exclaimed in admiration of his long-dead predecessor.

In a little tomb, dim, silent, pervaded by a sense of complete detachment from life and time, Mohamed showed Mary a wall painting of a youth and maiden kneeling over a millet mortar. Their labour had ceased for a moment. Their lips met in a delicately amorous interlude.

"Isn't it exquisite? The Egyptians never kissed, that is, in their tomb wall paintings—this is very sad, very beautiful, I think. And it is a kiss that lasts for ever, here in the darkness since two thousand years!"

He smiled at his companion, her lips slightly parted as she looked wonderingly at the long-dead lovers. Then firmly, his hands on her arms, he turned her towards him, his eyes shining. Very firmly but gently he pulled her towards him and with his lips on hers held her in a long silence. She made no motion, quiescent; the warmth of his flesh flowing through her in that chill tomb. Then he released her, as gently as he had taken her to him. She was trembling, and looked at him, wide-eyed.

"Why did you do that, Mohamed?" she asked.

"I have wanted to do that for a long, long time—you are so beautiful, Mary. You are not angry? Here, with these lovers before us, and away from your aunt, I could not——"

"My poor aunt, waiting out there in the blazing heat—we must go," said Mary.

"Happily she does not like tombs—unhappily she does not like me; she thinks me a bad man!"

He laughed as he said this, his hands again on her arms.

"Are you a bad man, Mohamed?"

"A little, sometimes!" he responded candidly.

He looked at her like a reproved schoolboy, then suddenly, in a gust of passion, he caught her to him. For a moment she resisted him, but his ardour bore her down and she relaxed under the frenzy of his kisses. Then she pushed his head away, releasing herself.

"Oh, my lovely one, my lovely one!" he cried, his face trembling with passion.

"Mohamed, we must go!" she said, breaking away from his arms. "You must control yourself!"

"You are not angry, you are not angry?" he asked persistently.

"I'm frightened. You must not do this—or I can never come with you."

He caught her hand and kissed it.

"My little dove—I would not frighten you. Forgive me, please!"

"You are forgiven—now, we must go."

"You will not tell Auntie—I fear Auntie! If I were Pharaoh I would seal her up in a tomb for ever!" he said with a laugh, following her.

"If you were Pharaoh I fear you would do many wicked things," replied Mary.

"Ah, you think me a very bad man?" he asked. "Why, because you are young and beautiful and I want to love you—it is not kind!"

"Have you no inhibitions?"

He stopped walking up the dark incline towards the portal of blazing light.

"What a word for a young girl! They taught you that at school?" he asked.

"My school was a good one. It had a large vocabulary! We didn't emerge green," said Mary, her candid eyes on his face.

"Green—how could you emerge green! You have the complexion of a summer rose in an English garden."

Mary burst into laughter. He regarded her in puzzled wonder, his pride hurt.

"By green we do not mean a colour. We mean that we know how to look after ourselves when we meet handsome and ardent young Egyptians."

He stared at her, wordless, then he said very quietly,

"That is unkind—if we made love, as I would like to make love with you, it would be a very wonderful thing—it would be an immortal moment. We would be like those lovers on the wall."

"Possibly. But you forget the next picture the artist did not draw."

"The next—what mean you?"

"In the second picture, Mohamed dear, it is twenty years later. She's grinding the millet alone, wrinkled, with sagging breasts, worn out with childbirth, while he runs around the village seducing young girls!"

Mohamed leaned back on the wall, his black curled head against the pale gold stone of a hieroglyphic panel in which Osiris judged the dead.

"What a terrible education you have in England!" he said earnestly. "You learn not to be green, as you say. You walk always with old vultures—I beg the pardon of Mrs. Cavan, but I speak plainly—and you scoff at the ecstasy of love, which is a divine gift."

He was so solemn as he made his declaration that Mary broke into laughter.

"Mohamed, if we don't go to the old vulture quick, she'll come in and tear you to pieces!"

He shrugged his shoulders, all the gaiety gone from his face. They walked towards the bright world beyond the portal.

II

Mohamed never alluded again to the incident in the Valley of the Kings. He left for Cairo the next day and when they met again he was agreeable to "the old vulture", and gravely correct towards Mary. Feeling that she had hurt him a little, she was glad when he returned to Luxor and invited them to his party on board the *Lotus*. Two weeks had elapsed since they had met.

"I am happy," said Mohamed, dancing with her. "Your aunt likes my mother. It is lucky for us!"

"Lucky? What do you mean?"

"While my mother entertains your aunt we can have more freedom together. Set a chaperone to catch a chaperone."

"Mohamed, you are very wily," commented Mary.

"For why am I an Egyptian, with all the lore of the Pharaohs?" he asked with a laugh, his beautiful teeth shining in the moonlight as he held her close to him.

"This is our last dance together—you must attend to your other guests. We must go, it's nearly two o'clock," said Mary.

"Tomorrow night there's a full moon. I have a plan. Let us sail on the Nile and then just before dawn we will go ashore and visit the Colossi of Memnon. Perhaps, as reputed, one of them will sing in the dawn."

Mary knew those two vast stone figures seated on the flat plain before the great amphitheatre of the Libyan hills. They had sat there, colossal, inscrutable, through thirty-five centuries, one of the wonders of the world.

"I'm afraid I couldn't persuade Auntie to stay up until dawn in the hope of hearing a Colossus sing—if ever it does," said Mary.

"The phenomenon is not so strange. It is believed to have made a singing note because the wind, rising at dawn, passed through a crevice in the head of the statue—the ancients, of course, thought it was the Colossus singing."

"The real phenomenon would be getting my aunt to stay up until dawn," said Mary dryly.

Mohamed Kafi smiled down at his partner. "Need she?" he asked quietly, and, as she looked at him, continued in a soft, low voice, "Tomorrow night, at one o'clock the moon is at its zenith. I shall come alone in the launch and wait by the water-gate of your villa. You will slip out. Could anything be more romantic? The Nile, a full moon, a picnic in the launch, a journey from the Arabian shore to the Libyan, a donkey ride over the sleeping plain, with all the dead Pharaohs in their rock tombs in the valley. We will watch the dawn come, rose-red, out of the east, and with the first flight of the birds across the water you will return to your nest. While Auntie sleeps we shall drink enchanted wine in moonlit Egypt."

"All very beautiful nonsense, Mohamed, but a girl can't play truant from the house where her Auntie sleeps. What if Auntie wakes?"

"Auntie will not wake."

"But how do we know? Anyhow, the whole thing's moonshine!" protested Mary.

"Moonshine—yes, beautiful moonshine! Auntie will not wake. You give her something."

"What do you mean?"

"I give you something to put in Auntie's coffee and she sleeps a long time, and wakes more happy in the morning. I know. My mama has slept like that."

"You mean you've drugged your mother!" exclaimed Mary, looking sharply at him. "But that's monstrous!"

Mohamed held her closer to him as a flute rose plaintively above the soft beating of a drum. A felucca with its white sail slid by like a ghost down the silver stream.

"Drug is not a nice word," he said. "We call it a sedative. It is not monstrous. Interfering mamas and aunties are monstrous when they stop lovers enjoying the moonlit night and the rosy dawn."

"Mohamed, you are a wicked poet. After that Egyptian fairy-tale I must go. Thank you for a most lovely evening. I must collect Auntie," she said, as the band stopped.

"I will take you to Mrs. Cavan," he said, escorting her from the deck. "Tomorrow night, at one o'clock, I will come, soft as a butterfly, to your water-gate."

"You mean silly as a moth—and you won't find as much as a candle to burn you!" retorted Mary.

He smiled, pressing her arm, but made no reply. The

seriousness of his mad proposal was emphasised when, later, he handed Mrs. Cavan and Mary down into their launch. As his hand left Mary's he pressed a small piece of folded paper into her palm. When, later, she surreptitiously unwrapped it she found a small white tablet. She threw it into the Nile.

"What a perfect night and what a lovely party!" exclaimed Mrs. Cavan. The moon had gone down. The launch left a faint trail of silver over the black velvet of the Nile. The Villa Bonjour, nestling behind its palms, came into view. Abu Omar brought the launch deftly aside the landing at the water-gate.

"Mohamed is a wonderful host—I begin to get quite fond of him as one understands him better," said Mrs. Cavan. "He is so sweet with his mother. It is a side of him I never expected."

"With Mohamed I suspect every side of him," said Mary quietly.

Her aunt looked sharply at her niece.

"Isn't that a little unkind? He's really been very attentive to you. Of course he's in love with you, but he must know there's no question of marriage. Your father would never consent. Anglo-Egyptian marriages are too difficult."

"I don't think we need consider refusing something that won't be offered," said Mary peremptorily.

Her aunt, surprised by the tone of her niece's reply, looked sharply up, but anything she might have said was checked by the assistant boatboy, who offered his arm for landing.

III

The next day, towards evening, Mary could hardly concentrate on her aunt's chit-chat. When Ibrahim, the butler, brought the coffee on to the terrace after dinner her mind was on Mohamed's proposal more than ever. Now was the moment when he had calmly proposed she should drug her aunt as a preliminary to a nocturnal adventure with him.

At the time she had half-suspected he was jesting, but when she found the tablet pressed into her hand she knew he had been in earnest. Did they do things like this in Egypt? Was Mohamed, for all his charm, exquisite manners and European education, just a calculating seducer? If that was his goal, doubtless he scored many successes. Handsome, wealthy, adept—with the capitals of Europe for his playground, it was ridiculous to think that he allowed himself to be frustrated. He must be irresistible to a great number of his prey. If Prince Salah had the same appetite he was more diffident in pursuit. Never once had he attempted to kiss her, never once had his touch lingered, though his eyes and voice had caressed her. A shyness pervaded his attentions. He lacked Mohamed's faun-like audacity, but it might be that the quieter manner hid the deeper intent.

It was ironical, recalling Mohamed's suggestion about the sleeping-tablet, that her aunt, while sipping her coffee, should begin to complain of two sleepless nights.

"I'm usually such a good sleeper, but of course I was too excited by the party last night and the late hour we got back to get off to sleep at once. I hope I'm going to have a good night tonight," said Mrs. Cavan. "I'm very tired."

Almost as if in echo Mary heard herself saying—"Do you ever take a sleeping-pill?"

"Well, since you ask, I'll confess that I do—very occasionally. I have a horror of drugs, but Dr. Clark, before I left home, gave me some tablets. He assures me they're quite harmless. I shall take one tonight, in case I can't get off."

How extraordinary! Here was Aunt Helen doing just what Mohamed desired, but it happened to be a voluntary act. How surprised her aunt would be if she told her of his astonishing proposal. With difficulty she refrained from enlightening her and changing her opinion of Mohamed's sweetness to his mother.

At half-past ten Mrs. Cavan, feeling very sleepy, announced her departure to bed. "I shan't need any pill to get me off tonight, I'm sure. I'm dead tired. I don't really believe this climate is good for me. It's too relaxing. What it must be like when the khamsin blows I can't imagine."

They both retired to their rooms. Ibrahim went round fastening windows and putting out lights. Soon the villa was nothing but a silent block of whitewashed sandstone glimmering amid the moonlit palm trees.

Mary did not go to bed. She sat at her secretaire writing letters. She was wide awake, and singularly restless. The moonlight lay like snow in the garden below her window. The great waxen trumpets of the datura hung in the still air above the beds where the night-blooming cereus gleamed luminously with its yellow corona. The scent of tuberoses filled the room, sickeningly sweet in the still night.

After a time Mary rose from her desk and went out on to the balcony of her room. The deep Egyptian sky sparkled with crystal stars above the great flood of the Nile beyond the wall of the garden. The moon had not yet risen, but a faint light lay over the water on which a few boats, with golden portholes gleaming, could be seen noiselessly riding downstream. A very faint sound of music came from the direction of the Winter Palace Hotel. They were dancing on the built-out terrace in the great garden with its palms, cascades of crimson bougainvillea and exotic plants. Not a leaf stirred in the warm night except the faint music and the intermittent croak of bull-frogs in the lotus pond.

Towards midnight Mary slowly undressed, brushed her hair and, finishing her toilet, got into bed. The night was so warm that she threw off everything except a linen sheet. She picked up a book and began to read. The words went past her without meaning. She turned out the light, but her mind was wide awake. Twelve struck in the little French clock on the mantelpiece, then the quarter. The room had become lighter, the moon was rising. Finally, exasperated by her lack of sleep, she got up and went on to the balcony. The world lay bathed in the light of the queen who had risen over the Arabian desert. Someone was singing now in a boat on the Nile, a boy's voice accompanied by a flute. She knew the voice, it was that of their own boatboy, Kissam, silver clear. He earned money by singing for the tourists who went out on midnight boat parties on the Nile. The whole night instead of turning to sleep had come alive, everything sentient in the moonlit landscape of Egypt.

Across on the foreshore, moored by the Libyan bank, shone the lights of half a dozen dahabeeyahs, row on row of golden discs where their portholes sent long reflections over the water. A few boats were moving up and down stream, white-sailed feluccas, and low launches with port and starboard lanterns gleaming over the water, the faint chug-chug of their propellers sounding in the distance.

Mary watched from her balcony for a while. Across there, somewhere among that line of lights, lay the *Lotus*. At the stern of the great dahabeeyah was tethered Mohamed's cream launch, low and swift in the water. Did he really intend to cross the Nile and expect to find her waiting for him at the landing? Was the whole proposal, the sleeping-tablet, the excursion over the plain to the Colossi of Memnon to hear the singing of the statue at dawn, all a joke? The proposal seemed as unreal as it was audacious.

She went back into her bedroom, lit only by the moonlight outside, and lay down. This nocturnal excursion with a secret flight from the villa, a return at dawn, with its risks, had an alluring element. No other scene in the world provided such a setting for adventure. If Mohamed came it would be folly to go. But had any other girl in the whole world such an enticing adventure offered to her, the Egyptian night, the broad shining Nile, the mysterious plain with its rock precipices holding the dynasties of the Pharaohs, those strange stone statues of the Colossi guarding the valley of Time, and a dark, handsome escort, who brought a human hazard to the whole adventure?

It was not difficult to leave the villa. She could go down

the stairs, half-lit by moonlight, into the drawing-room, out by the french window, then across the terrace and on to the lawn. For twenty yards she would be visible in the garden, but there would be no danger of detection by the servants, whose quarters were behind the villa. The window of her aunt's room overlooked the garden. It was most probable that she was now fast asleep. After all, why should she not go out into the garden on a warm, beautiful night? And if detected at dawn she could plead early rising.

She lay in the darkness considering the whole thing. The sense of adventure stimulated her mind. If Mohamed presumed on her position she would firmly deal with him. At the best she must assume he was a gentleman merely desiring a pleasant adventure. She could deal with anything in his manner that suggested liberties with her person.

She sat up in her bed. What was she considering? If he came and she went with him she was embarking on an unpredictable adventure. Young girls did not go out at night alone, in launches, with amorous young men, particularly young men of Oriental blood.

She lay down again. The French clock struck half-past twelve. She was so very wide awake. The moon, now a great disc climbing the sky, had flooded the garden, making everything visible. The palms seemed immense, silhouetted against the bright dome. Suddenly she rose, switched on the bedside lamp and began to dress. She would go down to the river front. There was a seat under the banyan tree. There, in the black shade, she would wait and see if Mohamed came. It was probable he would not; she had told him that no candle would be burning for a silly moth.

IV

It was surprising how alive the Nile was on this night of the full moon. She could see everything very clearly. Half a dozen feluccas were tacking in the faint breeze coming from

the Libyan bank. Voices came across the flood, and music.
Some Arab boatmen were languidly wailing dirges that filled
in the native atmosphere for tourists seeing the Nile by night.
The soft wind was aromatic. Again and again she saw the
green and red lights of a launch coming towards the water-
gate of the Villa Bonjour, but each in turn passed without
coming close inshore. She must have been sitting under the
banyan tree for half an hour. As she went forth in the moonlight to look at her wrist-watch she saw a launch make a
half-circle upstream and then turn in towards the water-
gate. She knew by its shape and the soft purr of its motor
that it was Mohamed Kafi's launch. It drew slowly along the
floating stage, and a youth sprang out from the stern, holding a rope. Mohamed followed, dressed in light brown
shantung trousers and a white shirt. He wore a scarlet fez
that emphasised the darkness of his face in the moonlight.

He hesitated for a moment, looked around and then
mounted the two steps of the water-gate and passed through
into the garden. He again hesitated and looked around.
Suddenly he saw Mary. He went towards her, smiling.

"Good evening. The silly moth has come to the candle,"
he said, smiling, doffing his fez.

"I wanted to see if you were really as audacious as you
pretended," said Mary.

"On such a night as this, as your Shakespeare said,
who would not be audacious? You've not disappointed
me."

"I suppose you were certain I would be here?" she asked,
resentful of his easy assurance.

"Yes," he said frankly, smiling at her with his dancing
eyes. "I relied on your sense of adventure. Auntie is fast
asleep?"

"I threw your tablet in the river—how could you be so
preposterous!" answered Mary.

"Then, she is fast asleep without a tablet—good! Let us
be going."

"I am not going. I was just curious to see if you could really be serious."

"In the presence of a beautiful woman I am always serious when I make a proposition. Come, let us go."

"I tell you I am not going!"

"Is that reasonable or kind? Having come out from the villa, why not enjoy the adventure? There will never be such another night as this. Mary, be sensible—do come, my dear," he pleaded.

"Whom have you with you?"

"No one, only the boatboys. Moussa and his young brother. They see nothing, hear nothing, say nothing, like the monkeys of Nikko."

"You have them well trained from practice, doubtless," commented Mary.

"I have all my servants well trained. Let us go, we will have a picnic in moonlight. I have a basket of the most delectable things. We will feast among the ghosts of the dead Pharaohs, we will see the moon go down and the dawn come blood-red from the east."

"It sounds like an Arabian Night's Dream—but no, Mohamed. Good night."

He moved closer, caught at her hand and raised it to his lips. Then he looked solemnly into her eyes.

"My darling, have no fear. You will be safe with me. It shall be whatever you desire. Come—it will all be so beautiful!"

He pleaded, his voice low, his eyes grave. Then he loosed her hand and stood silently before her. The sound of flute music came again on the night breeze. A wide-winged bird flew in from the river through the silver night. The earth breathed enchantment.

"Very well, I will," said Mary.

He caught her hand, his face suddenly joyous, and led her towards the waiting launch.

V

The launch turned upstream and soon had left the lights of Luxor. The Nile under the moon was like a silver lake, and where the prow of the boat cut the current two divergent streams of water reflected the moonlight in a wake of scintillating ripples. Presently the boat turned into a side canal embowered in palm trees, then it slowed down, and finally stopped. A small anchor went overboard as the engine was cut off.

"Where are we?" asked Mary, her voice low in this miracle landscape of moonlight, water and palm trees.

"We are in a backwater that leads to Naga-al-Gast from which there is a track leading to the necropolis of Thebes and the Colossi of Memnon. Look!"

He pointed to a vista beyond the dark tunnel of palms. There in the moonlight, mysteriously shining, was the towering rock amphitheatre that held the tombs of the Pharaohs, etched in the grey and blue of this luminous night.

The boy who had been at the wheel was joined by another. Their long robes were snow-white in the moonlight, contrasting with their swarthy faces, open throats, dark hands and naked feet. They deftly set a small table in the middle of the launch. From baskets they had soon produced various foods and bottles. It looked a Lucullan feast.

"Now let us eat," said Mohamed boyishly, piling up cushions for Mary's back. The elder boy remained to wait at table, the other disappeared. Presently as they ate there was a sound of music, plucked from a string instrument, half-guitar, half-violin, played pizzicato. A high voice began to intone. The voice added to the mysterious enchantment of the night.

"Who is that?" enquired Mary, as the first notes broke through the silence of air, water and trees.

"That's Lalifu, one of my boatboys. I bought him five years ago from a dealer in eunuchs near Badhour in the

Red Sea—so his voice will never break. Is he not exquisite—listen to my nightingale!"

The thin plaintive voice trembled in the hushed night.

"You bought him? But that's horrible! Surely such things aren't allowed! There's no slave traffic today!"

"I wish that that were true, my dear girl," replied Mohamed, "but all the way down the Red Sea shore destitute parents come to sell little boys and girls, sometimes their own, sometimes stolen children. The authorities are beaten in the game. Faster than they can move are the dhows hanging offshore for their cargoes out of Sudan and Abyssinia. The slave traffic, they will tell you, is dead. Don't you believe it. Your Government and mine signed a Convention in 1877 abolishing slavery. It was to come into operation in the Sudan in 1889. Your General Gordon found he simply couldn't work it and published a Proclamation in 1883 in Khartoum stating that whoever had slaves should have a right to their services and full control of them. That created a rumpus in England among your anti-slavers.

"One winter I went to Djibouti, for some gazelle-hunting, but I had no luck. I ran into a little one-eyed Frenchman, Jean Benoit. I think he had deserted from the Foreign Legion. I'm sure he was a criminal. He confessed to being in the hashish traffic. He told me there was wonderful turtle-fishing up coast. So I hired a felucca with a crew of Danâkalis, dark-skinned fellows out of the southern Sudan. We set off for the Swaba islands that lie in the southern part of the Suez, between the Yemen and Eritrea. We had little luck there, so he suggested that we moved on to Kohr Nowarat. It's almost a lake connected by a treacherous strait with the sea. In the middle of the strait, desolate and hot as hell, is the island of Badhour. He said there was good pearl-fishing there. Benoit knew everybody, every lair, every kind of traffic that passed over those waters. I knew well he was in every racket there was, aphrodisiac peddling—they get it from sea slugs by burning the membrane, and India

will pay fabulous prices for it—hashish, slaves and boy
eunuchs. The people on Badhour are Arabian in blood.
They look down on the Sudanese living along the coast,
mongrels in their eyes—but what magnificent mongrels!
They've got Egyptian blood mixed in them. The Khedives
had slave drives for them in the old days. You can see them
today decorating hotel lobbies in Cairo, decked out in
Oriental robes, porters, doormen and coffee makers. They
have an additional form of livelihood. With their massive
figures, their muscled naked bodies and ebony skins, they
get employment in the dancing dens and night clubs all over
Egypt. The boys of the tribe are the handsomest specimens
alive, and were always in great demand by the slavers.
Sometimes they bought the boys, sometimes they raided the
coastal villages and stole them. There was some sort of
entrepôt around Badhour where this traffic flourished.

"One day Benoit, who had been missing from our boat all
the previous evening, came alongside in a skiff. When he had
boarded he asked if I wanted to buy a magnificent boy, a
Sudanese, and his young brother, who had the singing voice
of a cherub. They were in the skiff. The most evil-looking
Somali I ever saw sat there with two naked boys crouched
beside him. He made them stand. One was a lad of fourteen,
muscled like a young boxer, the other, the singing boy, was
about twelve. I didn't know then he'd been emasculated.
I didn't believe a word of the story, of course, that the
Somali was their father, for the boys were half-Arab, half-
Sudanese. Neither did Benoit. He said he was sorry for the
lads, they were going to be shipped surreptitiously up the
Red Sea to Jeddah, for God knows what sort of a life. I knew
the whole transaction was illegal, but I felt upset about
those boys. I bought them. And here they are, happy and
devoted to me. They know they could go off tomorrow, but
they won't!"

He addressed the tall youth in a white robe and crimson
sash. He had been at the tiller while they crossed the Nile,

now he was the perfect waiter at table. Mary noticed how deft were his movements and how slender were his long dark hands as he handed the plates. He walked silently, barefoot, with great grace. The open robe revealed an ebony neck like a tower springing from a powerful chest, yet he had an air of slenderness.

Whatever it was that Mohamed Kafi said to him there must have been some reference to his guest at the table. He put his hands to his brow and bowed solemnly. Then his dark face broke into a smile. Mary noticed how his strong white teeth gleamed in the moonlight.

"This is Moussa, the elder boy. I would trust my life with him anywhere, and he's no mean chef. It's his work tonight," said Mohamed, by way of introduction.

"What a wonderful supper. Thank you, Moussa," said Mary, smiling up at the youth.

"You ver' kind, mees. Mohamed Effendi ver' kind let me cook for butiful ladee."

"Why, he speaks English!" exclaimed Mary.

"A little. Last winter when I was in America I sent him as a page to the Palace Hotel. He learnt a little English there, and other things not so good. He also learned to cook."

The boy on the prow was singing to his lute. He had a pure light voice, but what he sang filled Mary with astonishment. Instead of the wailing half-tones of Africa he was singing a plaintive Irish air.

"You recognise it?" asked Mohamed, laughing.

"Why it's *She's far from the land* . . .!"

"Good, but the words you can't possibly understand, though Lalifu thinks he's singing English! You see, I had an Irish nurse and she used to sing Irish airs to me. Lalifu will give us *O My Dark Rosaleen* presently. Their native music means nothing to our ears, so I thought it would be fun to make him sing my old nanny's songs. The boy's fluent in Italian, he must have spoken it as a kid, probably from the scoundrel who mutilated him in Somaliland. I have plans for Lalifu. One day I shall take him to Rome. I've already spoken to a Catholic Father there. We shall try to get him in the Sistine Chapel choir. They used to have *castrati* in it, so it'll be going back to an old tradition."

"What happens to the little girls; are they in the traffic also?" asked Mary.

"We will not talk about what happens to the little girls. I'm told they fetch only half the price of a boy. I cannot help smiling ironically when I hear the big-mouthed politicians passing solemn resolutions on the abolition of the slave trade. Next to prostitution it's the oldest traffic in the world. No Arab or African can understand the European hullaballoo about it. Even the enlightened Greeks ran slave markets. Fifty thousand passed through Delos every year. The Koran recognises slaves to this day."

The boy had ceased singing. Mohamed clapped his hands and he came forward very gravely and bowed.

"But he's beautiful!" exclaimed Mary, looking at the boy's face. It was fine in every feature.

"Yes, quite an Adonis, and a monkey for mischief."

"Canta l'aria 'Celeste Aïda' per la signorina, Lalifu," said Mohamed.

"Si, si, Effendi," responded the boy, raising the lute hung from his neck. The pure strains of the *Celeste* rose up into the still night. How odd seemed this transposition of Verdi from Japan to Egypt! When the boy had finished singing, Mary clapped her hands. He bowed very low and smiled engagingly.

"May I give him something?" asked Mary.

"Please, no. I don't want him spoilt."

He spoke to the boy, who retired back to the prow of the launch.

"Of all the strange things—to hear Verdi sung on a backwater of the Nile! You are an astonishing man, Mohamed."

"It is not so strange, my dear. After all, Verdi wrote *Aïda*

on the Khedive's commission, in honour of the opening of
the Suez Canal by the Emperor of the French. It was first
performed in the Opera House at Cairo at a gala performance. Hence the libretto about an Egyptian general who
turned down a Pharaoh's daughter for a captive Ethiopian
princess."

A cork popped. Mary looked at Mohamed.

"Not champagne?" she exclaimed.

"Why not? This is a gala performance in honour of a girl
with the courage to give Auntie the slip and come out into
the night with a crafty Egyptian!" he said, laughing. "But
we shan't be buried alive!"

"I fear you are very crafty."

"Very! I have you here, after all!"

"It's delightful! You're a magician. Moonlight, water, a
singing boy, champagne! I hope you're not putting any
tablets in this champagne!" cried Mary.

He took her glass in exchange for his. They touched rims,
and drank looking into each other's eyes. Presently Lalifu
began to sing again.

"What is he singing—it's Oriental?"

"Yes—he's singing a Sudanese folk-song. It's not very
romantic. It's about a man whose ugly wife was changed
into a gazelle, but she was as useless as she was beautiful. So
he took her back to the magician who changed her into a
goat. Again the owner was exasperated, the goat was obstinate. He had it changed into a camel. He was happy then.
He could beat her and ride her and, when she grew old, sell
her skin."

"The women have a poor time of it here!" observed Mary.

"Some women, but other women are queens in Egypt,
like Hatshepsut, Nefertiti, Cleopatra—and you!" said
Mohamed, leaning towards her, glass in hand.

"Thank you, Pharaoh!"

He took her hand and kissed it, as Moussa's back was
turned.

"How beautiful you are!" he said quietly.

"A gazelle, in fact," retorted Mary. "But I decline to become a camel."

They burst into laughter.

"No magician could transform you into a camel! You are the magician and I am at your mercy."

"Thank you. That makes me feel a little safer."

"You are not afraid?" he asked, opening wide his dark eyes. He took the champagne bottle and was about to fill her glass.

"No—not again, thank you," she said, drawing the glass away. "What time is it?"

He looked at his wrist-watch.

"It's early yet—half-past two. Dawn comes up about four. I must be honest, Mary. I joked about the Colossus singing. It ceased singing after the Roman Emperor Septimius Severus repaired the crack in its head. At the beginning of the Empire, after the statue had been broken, it emitted a musical sound at sunrise. Alas, Septimius with his renovation killed the phenomenon. I'm sorry, but we shan't hear the Colossus sing."

"I've heard Lalifu—I'm sure he's a better singer, so I'll forgive you," said Mary.

Moussa removed the little table.

"We'll go downstream now to the landing at Naga-el-Töd," said Mohamed.

In half an hour journeying down the mirror-like river they came to the landing. Mary knew it well now, after various excursions to the Theban necropolis. The launch tied up, and as they came ashore in the moonlight two men in brown robes approached Mohamed and saluted him. They were the donkey boys who would take them through the meadows and the scattered villages of huts that covered the plain where once the far-famed hundred-gated city of Thebes had brought its dead for communal interment. Tonight all was silver grey where the fellahin slept in little settlements marked by the cluster of palms that gave them shade in the heat of the day.

The land here was lushly green with crops of wheat, barley and flax, and interlaced with little irrigation canals on whose banks stood those engines of the fellahin's slavery and salvation, the *shadûf*, primitive water-wheels by which, laboriously turning them, the half-naked peasants lifted the water from the canals into the runways of the cultivated fields. Thus it had been in the days of the Pharaohs, thus it was today. And when the water ceased to be lifted, to perform its life-giving magic, the desert came back, the barren, merciless desert that bounded Egypt to the east and the west, so that the living Egypt was only a narrow carpet of green marking the track of the Nile meandering through eight hundred miles of its scorched journey, from the arid sands of Nubia to the green marshlands of its delta on the Mediterranean Sea.

After half an hour's slow donkey-ride through the silent landscape they drew up before a low building shadowed by a thick grove of palm trees. Mohamed dismounted and came to Mary.

"What is this?" she asked.

"It is my private rest-house," he said, helping her down.

"Your rest-house?" she asked as they walked in the dark avenue towards a gate.

"Yes—I keep it for picnics when we make excursions. I don't like to be mixed up with the tourists in Messrs. Cook's rest-house. This is my retreat. It is primitive and ancient. Part of it was once an embalming school kept by the priests of Amon who had embalmers trained here."

He unlocked a door under a heavy stone portico. A dim electric bulb burned in a narrow hall. At the end of the hall, open to the sky, a vivid oblong of white light, was a second doorway. He led her through to it and they stepped out into a small courtyard in the form of a peristyle. A huge black statue of Hathor, cow-headed, stood before the south colonnade, and another of the fox-headed Anubis, in the same black stone, stood before the north colonnade. Their heavy cubic bases were covered with engraved hieroglyphs.

"They come from the temple of Deir-el-Bahri. Aren't they fine fellows?" asked Mohamed, resting a hand on Anubis.

"How old are they?"

"Oh, possibly the Eighteenth Dynasty—fifteen to thirteen hundred B.C."

Mary stood in the moonlight, in the deep silence of the enclosed court with its great black statues. She thought of the endless generations of Pharaohs, High Priests, Court Officials, who had ceremonially paraded before them, on this same soil, under this same moon. The reality was dizzily beyond the imagination. The vast stone temples remained, with their only companions in Time, the long deep tombs where in the darkness, surrounded by symbols, and wall paintings with their cryptic meanings, the Pharaohs set forth on the fateful journey, accompanied by their *Ka*, the guardian spirit that, born with them, did not die but went with its protégés into the future world. When the god Thoret had weighed their hearts in the scales of righteousness, and they had been found perfect, and when the forty-two judges had found them free from sin, then Osiris judged them, condemning, or awarding them eternal happiness in the mountains of the west.

And here was the end of the story threading the dynasties —some carvings, a few statues, some broken temples, dark tombs—and the rest silence. It was as if the whole history of Egypt could be written in three simple statements: dust yesterday, dust today and dust tomorrow.

"You are very serious!" said Mohamed, looking down into his companion's face. "Come, I'll show you something."

There was an open stone staircase leading from the courtyard to the flat roof of the house. When they had gained the roof Mary stood spellbound by the panorama before her. Washed in the moonlight, the fields lay below her with their clusters of palms and peasant dwellings. They looked eastward towards the great shining river, with the ruined temple of Luxor along its bank, while beyond rose the pylons, obelisks and columns of Karnak—clear in the brilliant night. Modern Luxor lay between them with its hotels, in which a few lights still burned. Her eyes travelled to the dense palm groves behind the Villa Bonjour, and, grey in the far background, like a crouching animal, she saw the Arabian mountains. Behind her, as Mary turned, lay a vaster panorama, in the foreground the tremendous Colossi rising from the green plain, the foothills with the great pile of the Ramesseum and, far beyond, built into the precipice wall of gold-hued rock, the long dazzling façade of the temple of Deir-el-Bahri. Mile on mile, in ravines of these Libyan mountains, lay the tombs of Pharaohs buried with a magnificence that matched the splendour of their lives.

"Well—what do you think of it?" asked Mohamed, at her side. "I feel it's like landing on a crater of the moon. The human race was here thousands and thousands of years ago, and now is gone, with only crumbling temples and painted tombs to show the skeleton outline of their vanished glory. Why are we proud, why do we fret at Fate, why do we spend our years inhibited by precepts and catechisms that choke the brief pleasures of mortality?" He opened out his hands in a gesture of futility. "We are all like Ozymandias!"

"Who?"

"Ozymandias—what, you do not know your Shelley?"

He began to quote the verses in his musical voice.

> "*I met a traveller from an antique land*
> *Who said: Two vast and trunkless legs of stone*
> *Stand in the desert. . . . Near them, on the sand,*
> *Half sunk, a visage lies, whose frown,*
> *And wrinkled lip, and sneer of cold command,*
> *Tell that its sculptor well those passions read*
> *Which yet survive, stamped on these lifeless things,*

The hand that rocked them, and the heart that fed:
And on the pedestal these words appear:
'My name is Ozymandias, king of kings:
Look on my works, ye Mighty, and despair!'
Nothing beside remains. Round the decay
Of that colossal wreck, boundless and bare
The lone and level sands stretch far away."

There was a deep silence after he finished, heavy with the sense of Time.

"How beautifully you recited that!" said Mary, moved by the verses in their apposite setting. "You are a poet yourself."

"I am one of the lost poets of Egypt. I think I was walled up by Rameses II for a lampoon on his favourite dancing girl!" he said playfully. "And now I will show you my retreat. I allow no one to come on to this roof. Here is my kingdom, the space, the silence, the stars."

He walked across the flat roof towards a small room, with a latticed door of antique design. He opened the door. By moonlight she saw the interior. There was nothing but a large square bed, covered with a cream camel-hair rug, cushions, and a small table, with an Egyptian lamp.

"You sleep here?" asked Mary, stepping into the room.

"No," he said, his face hidden as he stood in the doorway, the moonlit sky behind him.

"It is for picnics?"

"No."

There was a pause, then he stepped in and stood beside her, looking down at her face.

"This could be the most wonderful night of our lives, dear girl," he said in a low voice.

"What do you mean?" she asked, her heart beating quicker as he took both of her hands.

Gently his arms went round her and his lips took hers, lightly, then more urgently. After a few moments she pushed him away, alarmed by his ardour.

"Don't let's be silly," she said, her voice unsteady.

"Silly—that is a very English word. We are here, we are young, we feel passion. The whole sense of fleeting time, the beauty of the night, call to us. What could be more wonderful than for us to lie here making love, my body against yours, my strength and your grace united in all the stillness and beauty of the night."

"But this is nonsense!" exclaimed Mary, drawing back.

He held her, his eyes burning, his voice hoarse with an undertone of passion.

"You are lovely as a dream, it is a moment such as may never come again. I will kneel down to worship you. Let us take off these stupid clothes hiding our flesh. Your naked body is the chalice of all beauty, mine is the consecrating flame. Let me hold you, your flesh to my flesh. We will be Cæsar and Cleopatra, Cupid and Psyche. We will dream here, alone in the moonlight, above the dead civilisations!"

His eyes were aflame and his voice trembled with passion as he pleaded. His hands held hers in a grip that was painful.

She looked fearlessly back into his eyes.

"How many times have you said all this in this place?" she demanded, a rising anger filling her voice.

"Mary!" he exclaimed. "Be reasonable!"

"You are, then, after all, a very commonplace Egyptian who entices a girl out to seduce her."

"Mary, I do not understand you—aren't you young, aren't you a woman, aren't you human?"

"I'm all those—but I am not a candidate for your harem, by moonlight or sunlight. Let us go!" she said in a firm voice.

He dropped her hands, and stood back.

"I have made you angry. I cannot understand why you will not take the pleasure of love."

"To be one of a dozen, two dozen, three dozen pick-ups? You must be crazy!" she retorted.

"I am crazy for your beautiful body. I offer you mine,

clean, strong, to give it you in worship. It is the most lovely thing in the world, two naked lovers embracing in the moon-light. It is the poetry of life! Why do you spurn it?" he asked in a hurt voice.

"In England young men don't take out girls they hardly know and ask them to undress in the moonlight."

"In England, no, it would be cold and rainy. The English have no heat in their flesh, but we Egyptians have passions, we drink the Libyan sun, we——"

"I think this is all very silly. Please let us go back to the launch at once. It was foolish to come!" cried Mary.

"Oh, you are now an angry miss—you look at me as the English spinsters look at a dragoman who has shown them a phallic tomb painting—they like it and they don't like it! Human beings in England don't caress beautiful bodies! How are you all born?"

"Mohamed, don't be so ridiculous!"

"Is it ridiculous that I want your body, to see it naked, curve on beautiful curve, to hold it, to caress it? What is the reason of youth? Why have we passions?"

"You grow more ridiculous. I'm a fool not to have fore-seen this was all planned. You've taken shameful advantage of my trust in you."

She looked at him angrily, her face flushed.

He spread out his arms despairingly and sighed heavily.

"I am most sorry. I beg your forgiveness. What I think poetry is for you filth, what I think a beautiful thing you find nauseating. The flame in us must be quenched. Forty years hence, if we are here, there will be no flame—there will be no longing in a body corrupted with years, a rose shrivelled, the perfume gone, the lonely dark valley of age remembering a flame that burned in the mountains. 'My name is Ozyman-dias, sport of things. Look on me, O ye Mighty and laugh loud'."

"I think you let words intoxicate you," said Mary. "It is you who should take a tablet to cool your flesh!"

She walked across the roof, and he followed, saying nothing.

Outside the donkey men were lying in the deep shade. She had a feeling they knew that their employer had been frustrated for once. They had settled down for a sleep, experienced in these nocturnal adventures.

Despite his importuning, Mary refused to wait for the dawn and view the Colossi of Memnon. They jogged back to the Nile bank with not a word between them. The moon was low in the sky, there was no glimmer of dawn.

They embarked, and then while they were in the middle of the river the dawn came up with a rush, blood-red out of Arabia, the upper heaven lemon-coloured, the cirrus clouds rimmed with rose, amid great pools of purple dissolving into an emerald sky. The tops of the palms caught the light. The Nile, incarnadined, was a burnished mirror. And then came the crystal light of day, a vast flood deluging the world, while the night retreated headlong into the desert ranges of Libya.

The launch came softly to the landing-stage. Lalifu was asleep on the foredeck, curled up like a kitten, only his black head visible. Moussa made fast the launch. Mohamed Kafi followed Mary to the water-gate.

"It is good-bye and good morning! Am I forgiven? I am most contrite, dear Mary," he said very quietly, serious-eyed.

"You are forgiven—it was so very beautiful until you spoilt it," said Mary.

He took her hand, bent low and touched it with his lips. Then as she turned to go the incorrigible boy in him could not resist a last word.

"I hope greatly that Auntie sleeps soundly, tablet or no tablet," he said with an impish smile.

Mary hurried through the gate. His wish was fulfilled. She reached her room undetected. It was a quarter to five.

CHAPTER IV

I

THE next morning, shortly before noon, Hamilton Bostowell arrived at the villa to everybody's surprise. His news was even more surprising. They were returning to England at once, the villa, its furnishings and the dahabeeyah were to be sold. It was unlikely that they would come back to Egypt again. Bostowell had not a good word to say for the Egyptians. He found them impossible to do business with, as they always shifted their ground. The long and tedious negotiations over a dam, subsidiary to the one nearing completion at Aswan, had come to nothing. Hoover Gould and Chester Wainwright had withdrawn in disgust from the negotiations. The only one who seemed to have found his part in the projected dam profitable was Mr. Moulmedji. It transpired that he had got them tied up in such a manner that there was nothing for them but to settle Mr. Moulmedji's claim for compensation. He had involved Bostowell so deeply that it cost the latter twenty thousand pounds to extricate himself.

"Six weeks of talk, ten thousand dollars in expenses, not counting Mrs. Gould's little excursion in the shops en route, and where are we? We never came within sight of a deal! Yes means No, and No equals Perhaps here!"

Hoover Gould chewed his cigar angrily as he paced the hotel sitting-room. He went to the window, turning his back on Bostowell and Wainwright. Across the Nile, above the houses on the embankment and the palm trees, a golden cone caught the sunset. It was the Great Pyramid of Gizeh.

"I wonder just how much graft that useless thing cost old Pharaoh?" he asked, staring at it.

"I'm told it cost the lives of forty thousand slaves. I suppose they thought it cheap at the price. At least it stands up. It is the only solid thing in Egypt," commented Wainwright.

"That, and the British," added Gould.

"I wouldn't be too sure of the British. We've got a bellyful trying to save them from corruption, drought and the bilharzi," said Bostowell.

"You must be getting something out of it or you British wouldn't make such an effort to stay," commented Gould sourly. "You'll lose the Dam, and you'll lose the Canal one day!"

"We should have known better," said Wainwright. "My bank in New York was against the whole damn' thing. Now I have to tell the boys they were right. No corn in Egypt for us!"

There was no corn in Egypt for Hamilton Bostowell. There seemed to be no corn anywhere just now. A hydroelectric works proposition in the Abruzzi had been turned down by the Italian Government after two years of negotiations. He had lost the flotation of a loan for Karachi; and a law case with the Inland Revenue, carried to the House of Lords, had gone against him with heavy costs. But Hamilton Bostowell was not a man to brood over his losses. He exuded good faith in himself. Early in April he took the most expensive suite on the *Orestes* out of Alexandria. Back in London he opened the house in Queen's Gate and began his lavish entertaining again.

At the end of April Cyril Ransome came home on two months' leave. He was constantly at the house, and assiduous in his attention to Mary Bostowell. She was to be presented at Court in June, and soon afterwards the announcement of her engagement to him would be made.

It was a brilliant season. London had never been gayer. It had recovered from the death of the great Queen, and now all preparations went forward for the magnificent coronation of her son, Edward VII. London began to fill with foreign royalties and statesmen.

In the spring of 1902, with a King to be crowned and the South African millionaires arriving in Park Lane to finance an aristocracy pinched by the rising income-tax and death duties following the South African War, London put on a brilliant social show. Every evening the red druggets were out in Berkeley Square, Park Lane and Knightsbridge. The massive strongholds of the upper middle-classes in Queen's Gate and Prince's Gate were staffed by five maids, two scullery maids, a cook, butler, pageboy, and a head and second coachman sleeping over the mews behind.

The new century with new ideas was beginning to change these mews. The younger coachman, since the older stubbornly refused, was sent to take lessons in driving a contraption that ran on petrol instead of hay. It was so erratic in performance that the older generation regarded it with derision and horror. The "fashion" still went about in a brougham with a pair of greys and a second footman on the box. The Lord Chamberlain was loudly applauded for flatly refusing to permit an eccentric earl to send his débutante daughter to her first Court in a motor-car; the queue of carriages waiting in The Mall was not to be contaminated by such an abomination. Towards dawn, in the height of the summer season, the clop-clop of hansom cabs, homeward bound after the ball, resounded throughout Mayfair and Knightsbridge.

In the second week of June, after Mary's presentation and shortly before the announcement of her engagement to Cyril Ransome, Hamilton Bostowell gave a ball at his Queen's Gate mansion. A small crowd gathered before the pillared portal to watch the guests arrive. Most of them were handsome and gay, the cream of London's young set. Eighty guests sat down to dinner, two hundred came to the ball in the long drawing-room that ran the whole depth of the four-storey house. The windows blazed with light, and out of them until dawn came the sound of dance music, of young voices and laughter.

Bostowell, Mrs. Cavan and Mary received the guests at the head of the staircase. The occasion had its crowning triumph with the presence of a royalty, an old Princess who stayed until one o'clock and made herself gracious to everyone. Mary danced every dance, giving half of them to Ransome, who was returning to Egypt in a fortnight's time. The Bostowell ball had a whole page of pictures in *The Tatler* and *The Sketch*. A group showed them with Her Royal Highness.

A week after the dance, Mary, returning from a luncheon party in Grosvenor Street, found an extraordinary atmosphere the moment she entered the house. Thompson, the grave Scots butler, was more than usually grave when he opened the massive front door and said that her aunt desired to see her in her room immediately. Mary went straight up to Mrs. Cavan's boudoir on the third floor. It was a pleasant room overlooking a garden with trees and a view of the Oriental tower of the Imperial Institute shining in the cloudless sky.

Mrs. Cavan, blanched, her genial face drawn with anxiety, rose and went towards her niece, took her in her arms and burst into tears.

"Auntie, whatever is the matter?" asked Mary.

Mrs. Cavan took out her lace handkerchief, wiped her eyes, and then screwed it up in nervous grief. Mary, feeling her tremble, led her to a chair and knelt beside her.

"Auntie, dear—what is it?" reiterated Mary.

At last the words came between choking sobs.

"About half an hour ago your father was arrested in his office and taken away by the police. Mr. Moberley, his solicitor, called me. That is all I know—he will call again after he has seen your father. What can it be, what can it be? He was quite cheerful when I saw him this morning before going to the City."

There was a tap on the door. Thompson appeared.

"They're on the telephone, madam. They want to come to the house. They want a photograph of Mr. Bostowell."

"Who—who's coming to the house?" asked Mrs. Cavan, distraught.

"The Press, madam," said Thompson.

"You must refuse to admit them," cried Mrs. Cavan, regaining her composure. "We haven't committed a murder!"

"Very good, madam. I will take off the receiver."

"Oh, not that—I'm awaiting a call from Mr. Moberley."

"Very good, madam."

"What have they arrested Father for, what can he have done?" cried Mary, holding her aunt's trembling hand.

"I can't think—unless he's been unfortunate with money matters. He's not been the same man since that Egyptian business came to nothing. Last night I was astonished to hear voices in the study as I went up to bed. I looked in and to my surprise found your father with that Armenian, Mr. Moulmedji."

"The man in Cairo—here!" cried Mary.

"There was something serious, for your father looked very alarmed, pushed me out of the room and locked the door. But he seemed quite calm again this morning at breakfast."

The door opened. Thompson came in.

"Mr. Moberley on the telephone, madam. He would like to speak to you."

Mrs. Cavan rose and followed him downstairs to the library.

"Mrs. Cavan?" asked a voice.

"Yes, speaking."

"This is Moberley. I have seen Mr. Bostowell. He will come up before the magistrates in the morning and be charged. We shall ask for bail. I fear he must remain in custody overnight. I am sending my clerk for some things he will require."

"Charged! Oh, Mr. Moberley, what is he charged with?" asked Mrs. Cavan.

"From what I gather at present, embezzlement and other things."

"But how? What——?" stammered Mrs. Cavan.

"It would be better not to talk on the telephone, Mrs. Cavan. I will communicate with you after court tomorrow. Meanwhile I would ask you to allow no one in the house, answer no questions on the telephone from reporters, tell the servants they must not let themselves be interviewed."

"We've already had the Press ringing up!"

"That's inevitable. Refuse to see them. The evening papers are already out with news of the arrest. Is Miss Bostowell there?" asked Moberley.

"Yes."

"Tell her I will come to see you both as soon as the case is heard tomorrow. We shall have to consider engaging counsel."

"Counsel—you mean Mr. Bostowell will not be set free?"

"I fear you must be prepared for his being sent for trial. The sums involved are very large. Good-bye—and be brave; we will do our best."

She put down the receiver. She knew Mr. Moberley, a little plump man in a black vicuna coat and pin-stripe trousers, with an office overlooking the fountain near Pump Court. He had been very efficient with a claim she once made against a fire insurance company which had quibbled. He took snuff and lived in a large Regency house at Sunningdale, where he followed his passion for breeding bulldogs.

Mrs. Cavan and Mary attempted dinner in a heavy silence. As they left the dining-room Thompson drew Mrs. Cavan discreetly aside.

"The evening papers are in the library, madam. I've put them under the lounge cushions, if you wish to see them."

"Thank you, Thompson."

In the library were four evening papers. Three of them had bold headlines: "Hamilton Bostowell, well-known company director, arrested in the City." There followed an account of his career, the long list of his best-known promotions. One paper had discovered a photograph. Oddly enough it showed him in a broad-brimmed white hat and yachting clothes on board the *Cherami*, "the millionaire's sumptuous yacht on the Nile", as it put it. There was a smaller photograph of Mary Bostowell, "the year's prettiest débutante", in her presentation dress and feathers. The news hit a London already stunned by King Edward VII's postponed coronation.

II

The proceedings in court the next morning were brief. Philip Hamilton Bostowell, of 22 Agincourt House, Lombard Street, was charged with embezzlement and fraud in a sum totalling £268,000. The defendant was committed for trial. The application for bail was refused.

That evening Mr. Moberley saw Mrs. Cavan and Mary. He could give them no comfort. "Very grave, very grave. The sum involved is very large—and there may be a charge of forgery also. We shall do our best. We are briefing Sir Gerald Formington. Could you not go away while this is on? The publicity will be very vexatious, I fear."

Mr. Moberley had just departed when Cyril Ransome arrived, very smart in his town clothes. Mary saw him in the library. He expressed his sorrow at the news. He was due to leave for Cairo in two days.

"Of course I could get extended leave, but the trial might not be for some time and go on and on," he said, looking at his hands nervously.

"You mustn't stay, Cyril. There's nothing you can do," said Mary.

"No—I suppose not. Well—er—what will you do?"

"I shall stand by Father, of course."

"Of course—naturally," echoed Ransome.

He fidgeted with his tie and paced up and down the carpet with his elegant long legs.

"Damn it—it's a staggerer—one can't believe it! And just when we were about to announce our engagement!" he said.

"I shall release you from that, Cyril," said Mary, looking at him.

He turned away, and played with an ornament on the mantelpiece.

"Well, all things considered, it would be better to wait, don't you think?"

The weakness of his thin handsome face seemed accentuated and pale above the light-grey double waistcoat with pearl buttons he was wearing. Mary, keeping back her tears, remembered how Mohamed Kafi had once called him "milk bred", which she had resented.

"If the trial goes all right, then of course——" he began hesitatingly.

She cut across his words, looking him in the face.

"And if the trial doesn't go all right?" she asked. "No, Cyril, I won't let you make any sacrifice."

"Oh, don't put it like that, Mary," he protested. "It isn't so much my position, but there's my people."

"Exactly," commented Mary. "You mustn't upset your people. So let's call it off. It will relieve them immensely."

"I say, you put it rather ruthlessly," he said.

Mary made no reply. There was an awkward silence.

"Do you mind, Cyril, if you leave now? I'm very tired."

"Oh, yes, of course you are. I'm sorry. I'll come and see you before I go. Perhaps it will all work out all right," he said, without conviction. "So don't lose hope."

"I'll try not to," responded Mary, as they went towards the door.

Mary saw him once again. They both knew well their affair was ended. He took his leave of her and of her aunt. Mary was calm as he went out of the door. Then, hurrying upstairs, she flung herself on her bed and cried to exhaustion. She never saw him again.

III

Hamilton Bostowell was sentenced to five years' penal servitude for embezzlement and fraud. He had for some years been desperately juggling. The judge was scathing. Bostowell did not serve the sentence. On his way down from the dock he collapsed. When a doctor was found, he was dead. He had taken potassium cyanide secreted somehow on his person. He must have foreseen this day of reckoning.

The shoot at Largs, a yacht at Cowes, the house and contents in Queen's Gate disappeared in a bankrupt's estate. Young Hamilton was taken from Summerfields and sent to live with his father's cousin in Montreal, who undertook to look after him. Mrs. Cavan, having a small villa in Majorca in which she lived on an army officer's widow's pension, took Mary with her. Within the year the world had forgotten the Bostowell case.

There was one surprising aftermath. One morning Mrs. Cavan received a letter with a Newport, U.S.A., postmark. It was from Mrs. Hoover Gould. "I am very grieved to hear what has happened," she wrote. "Mr. Bostowell was good company and a delightful host, and I thought Mary a very sweet girl. Things, I fear, must be difficult for her. Will you use the enclosed in some way for her benefit; it would give Hoover and me much pleasure."

The enclosed was a cheque for a thousand dollars.

CHAPTER V

I

THE Villa Hoya, Mrs. Cavan's Majorcan property, was situated on the mountainside near Puerto de Sóller. This was a small village, with a few summer hotels set round the bay on the north-west coast of the island of Majorca. The harbour, hemmed in by mountains, was almost enclosed, the sea entering between two jetties. Above one of the jetties, on the ledge of the mountain, was a white lighthouse; near the other jetty, in a long rambling building also painted white, there was a small naval training base. Puerto de Sóller lived in a dream. In the plain behind the port lay the village of Sóller amid its vines and orange-groves. It sat at the bottom of a cup made by the enclosing mountains. From this group rose the island's highest mountain, the Puig Mayor.

Sóller in the plain, if not reached by sea, was accessible by a road that came dizzily over the Col de Sóller mountain. There was also a railway, with a train, almost a toy affair, with curtained windows and bright brass fittings, that once daily made the journey from Palma. It travelled first through the vineyards and orchards of a great plain and then through eleven tunnels. Emerging from one of these, on the inside of the cup, high over Sóller, the train took a three-mile circuitous route above the village in its descent to the plain.

Sóller could not quite call itself a town although it boasted a plaza, a bank and a concert hall. It was very ancient, with narrow winding streets. The Moorish pattern seemed still there in the fortified strength of some of its houses with their shut-in courtyards. When the Sóller dancers, a lively team, gave an exhibition of native dancing, either by themselves or in competition with neighbouring Puerto or other hamlets, the men and women were attired in Moorish clothes, the men in wide baggy trousers tucked in below the knees, with white stockings and special Majorcan dancing shoes, the women in vividly coloured skirts and embroidered bodices. They danced with enormous verve to a wind and string orchestra.

In 1902 Sóller and Puerto had not been discovered by the tourists. The journey by boat from Barcelona to Palma, and then the journey by train to Sóller, placed it out of reach. Its native Majorcan population was increased by a small colony of foreigners, all very poor, a miscellaneous group of English, American and French writers and artists, mostly unsuccessful, but of unquenchable belief in their gifts. With their little villas set in the orange-groves, with beautiful views from all the windows, with an agreeable native population, very cheap living, and endless sunshine, they were a happy collection of people who, while they might be said to have unfulfilled their ambitions, had found here a halcyon retreat, washed by the blue Mediterranean sea, and remote from the everlasting unrest of the great world.

The Villa Hoya, half a mile out of the town, was a comparatively new house built by a Malaga lawyer for a summer retreat. It had three bedrooms, a sitting-room, kitchen and bathroom, and electric light. These rooms were all on an upper storey, which had a small terrace overlooking the plain and the great barrier of the mountains. The house was whitewashed inside and out except for a vivid blue wash that covered the arches and store rooms over which the living-rooms were placed. Mrs. Cavan rented this villa, furnished, and a half-acre of garden for £20 a year. She continued to live genteelly, practising small economies, on £200 a year, considered quite an income by the natives of Sóller. For some years her position had been eased by a yearly sum of £100 from her brother, who also paid all her travelling expenses when she came to visit him after Mrs. Bostowell's death. These periods grew longer and longer, but she retained the Villa Hoya for a retreat. It was fortunate she had done so. When the crash came it was to this modest home that Mrs. Cavan, with Mary, retired. They had little money, above all they wanted respite from the harrowing publicity. Cyril Ransome's abject retreat had left a deep wound in the girl's heart.

Aunt and niece settled in at the Villa Hoya. They rarely went down to the beach at Puerto, some two miles away, or into the town, a pair of recluses washed up by the unkind sea of Fate. The autumn and winter came and passed. They made a few friends among the colony; the stream of letters, sympathetic, dried up. With the aid of Mrs. Hoover Gould's cheque they procured a few extra comforts, above all an ample supply of wood fuel for the chilly winter evenings.

When the early spring came a restlessness began to invade Mary's mind. She could not go on living in this backwater on her aunt's tiny income. She began to look around for some means of income. She could go back to London and seek for an office job among some of her father's business acquaintances, but she shrank from the publicity she must face as Hamilton Bostowell's unfortunate daughter. It was ironical that some of the stigma on his name was already beginning to fade. Two of his company promotions had proved successful and were bringing in dividends. People began to say he had been unlucky with his timing and, hard-pressed, had fallen into fraud. Nevertheless, the thought of returning to London was unpleasant. Then, in March, Fate seemed to smile on her. An old friend of the family, half-English, half-Spanish, with interests in Anglo-Spanish companies, and a house in Seville, wrote to ask whether she would come to them for two years and prepare two children, a boy and a girl, for their preparatory school in England. The Harcourts lived in a pleasant house in Seville. There was a family of five. Mary would be very welcome. A modest salary was offered.

In March Mary left for Seville, and straightway walked

into a new life. The Harcourt family were delightful. Mrs. Harcourt, who was Spanish, was a large noisy woman, good-natured, untidy, with a tremendous zest for life. Mr. Harcourt was often away on business. The little boy was nine, the girl eight, there was a baby of four. The Harcourts lived in a large Spanish casa on the edge of the lovely Paseo de las Delicias, with its wealth of eucalyptus, myrrh, persimmon, palm and pepper trees. From the windows of her room she could see the shining, tawny waters of the Guadalquivir River and the famous Giralda Moorish prayer-tower, high above the roofs of the vast cathedral in which lay the much-travelled bones of Christopher Columbus.

The casa was surrounded by trees, and when Mary arrived every room was pervaded by the delicious scent of orange blossom. The establishment had five servants, a coachman and a groom. There were four horses in the stables. Every morning Mary went riding with Mrs. Harcourt along the Paseo de las Delicias.

Mary's advent had created a stir in the English and American colony. Her fair, rose-like beauty, her excellent figure and above all the warmth of her smile soon made her the most sought-after young woman in Seville by the English, American and Spanish youths. She had quickly picked up the language, she was an excellent dancer. Her story was of course known, and to admiration of her beauty was added sympathy for the ordeal she had suffered. She began to be entertained and saw the interiors of many of the Spanish houses with their lovely semi-tropical patios and beautiful iron grilles, their terraced flat roofs, their pots of scarlet geraniums, red carnations, orange-coloured arbutus, and pink and yellow hoya riding along the walls. And every-where there was white orange blossom scenting the air in the days before Easter, which saw the jewelled Madonnas carried through the streets to the cathedral in the frenzied religious ecstasy of Holy Week.

These were the nights of spring-time. In perfumed alleys

and courts around the ancient Alcazar, one heard guitars and the light laughter of dark-eyed señoritas, mantilla-clad, walking with narrow-hipped young swains in tight black trousers and jackets, coming from houses blazing with lights where a dance was being held. When the rays of dawn touched the Giralda tower, they went riding through the palm gardens and along the embankment of the Guadal-quivir, where boats from Cadiz tied up to unload their cargoes. It was sheer enchantment to Mary Bostowell after the nightmare she had known, this colour and gaiety in the city of Pedro the Cruel, Velasquez, Murillo, and Carmen, the girl of the great tobacco factory, with the red carnation provocatively stuck over one ear.

II

A happy year slipped away. One evening, coming through the exquisite Court of the Oranges, with its little orange trees in the shadow of the cathedral, a dapper youth accosted Mary's Spanish escort. He was introduced, but she did not catch the name, and for some time assumed he was English, so perfect was his speech. He insisted on their driving back in an open landau, waiting in the street, to his house, though it was past midnight. There were a coachman and a young groom on the box, in yellow-faced liveries.

Presently they came to a pair of massive grille gates which opened on to a carriage drive divided by a great fountain and basin in which bloomed exotic plants and crimson cannas. Beyond, enclosing three sides of this great forecourt with its imperial palms, stood the house. It was covered with wistaria in blue flower. The whole front of the first storey was arcaded and opened on to the patio.

Their young host, handing Mary down, led the party up a great staircase so shallow and wide that six horses might have been ridden up it abreast. They came to the long arcaded gallery with Spanish floor tiles. Here, a footman appearing, their host ordered refreshments. The sky was full of stars above the palms.

Mary could look at her host now. He was of medium height with a beautiful head, fine-featured. He exuded a natural gaiety. This house of his reflected considerable style and wealth. Later she learned that it was the famous Palacio de las Dueñas. Built in 1450 in the Moorish style around a great patio, its first owner had been captured in battle by the Moors. To raise his ransom the palace was sold and it passed to the Alba line, for their young and vivacious host was the seventeenth Duke of Alba and Berwick. He had Stuart royal blood in his veins from his English ancestor, James II, by a liaison with Arabella Churchill, sister of the great Duke of Marlborough. A Spanish ancestor was the great Duke of Alva. Vivacious, handsome, he was adored by his great-aunt, the Empress Eugénie, who had just left the palace for England. Young Alba had recently succeeded and he now found himself the owner of a dozen castles and estates throughout Spain. Modest, intelligent, his great inheritance sat lightly upon him.

Mary was destined to see much of "Jimmy", as his English friends called him. By the strange play of chance he was the means of the greatest event in her life. At one of the spring balls given by his mother, the Duchess, and honoured by the presence of Queen Christina and her stripling son, King Alfonso, Mary met young Lieutenant Miles Callender, R.N., the Duke's house guest for the *Feria*, the great spring horse carnival.

The great *Feria* opened in April, in the early Andalusian spring. From all over Spain came the connoisseurs of horses, for this was the world's greatest horse fair which not even Hungary could rival. In the great Prado, long avenues of booths were erected, under rows of suspended lanterns and illuminated arches. There, in a quadrangle of drives, the proud horsemen paraded. The *casetas*, or booths, lining the avenues, belonged to the various Confederations that com-

peted in the lavishness with which they were furnished.
Some of them were hung with tapestries and adorned with
antique furniture. Each *caseta* preserved a central dancing
place and here in the evenings, to the strumming of guitars
and the rattle of tambourines and castanets, the younger
members danced the *Sevillanas* while relatives and friends sat
round, applauding, gossiping and drinking. By night the long
parallel avenues were lined with thousands of red and white
lanterns. At the crossroads there were triumphal arches and
coronets of coloured electric lights. The blaze of these filled
the sky overhead with a roseate glow. All this was a setting
for the great daily horse parades which began soon after noon.

Reference being made to the forthcoming *Feria*, the young
duke suggested they should join his party. He had his own
caseta in the central avenue, with an orchestra for the evening
dances that went on till dawn.

"You must join us," he said to Mary. "I will send for you
and we'll drive to the *Feria* for the morning parade. I'm
having a house-party, about twenty guests."

The first day of the *Feria* opened, in glorious weather. All
Seville was *en fête*. It was orange-blossom time. The city of
the Moorish kings was crammed with tourists. A carriage
came from the Palacio de las Dueñas a little before noon and
took Mrs. Harcourt and Mary to join the house-party preparing to leave for the fairground. A dozen open carriages
stood in the patio, the grooms in the Alba livery, grey with
the yellow Alba cockades. The splendid mules in pairs, trios,
quartettes and quintos, caparisoned with harness bearing the
Alba crest, had their heads enmeshed in yellow and blue
cordage with hanging tassels.

A groom of the chambers led the guests to the waiting
carriages. The ladies wore wide flounced costumes that
billowed around them and overflowed the sides of the carriages. The leading carriage with the young duke, his friend
and two ladies, was a quinto, two grooms on the box seat,
and five mules with a postilion on the single leading mule.

The dresses of the two ladies, white silk, flounced with hundreds of pleats and floral in design, were thrown back over the lowered hood of the open landau and flowed down almost on to the wheels. The duke and his friend, young Prince Philip of Bourbon-Sicily, accompanied by his sister and Doña Eulalia of Orleans, both pretty girls in their early twenties, occupied the first carriage. The men wore tight blue bolero jackets, piqué cream waistcoats and broad-brimmed black Córdoba hats.

With a spirited clatter of horses and jingling of harness, their host's carriage set off down the sub-tropical patio and through the great gates into the street. A crowd in festive mood cheered the cavalcade and waved, saluting the lovely ladies and their escorts.

They arrived on the fairground at the hour of the grand parade. It was thronged by carriages and men and women on horseback all competing in the splendour of their equip-ages. Slowly they paraded, up one avenue and down another, passing the thronged *casetas* gaily decorated in this vast field of colour.

By good luck, or the young man's foresight, Mary found herself in a carriage with Miles Callender, among a party of four. She remembered him from the ball two nights earlier when the duke had introduced his English guest. He was a tall, slender young man, elegant in attire, with a singularly charming voice. He had just come out to Madrid as assistant naval attaché at the British Embassy. Fair, vivacious, he was an excellent dancer and found in Mary an ideal partner. They had had four dances together at the ball and sat at the same table for supper. Now they were confronting each other in the open carriage drawn by two pairs. Their excitement in this intoxicating spectacle was mutual. As they slowly moved in the long procession of carriages and the press of horsemen, they had time to notice individual participants. Some of the young Spaniards, magnificently mounted, in Andalusian riding-boots, tight trousers and short bolero jackets revealing narrow waists swathed in crimson silk sashes, carried their fair companions pillion-fashion. The girls' dresses with their flounced tiers flowed down over the haunches of the horses, on which they sat sideways so that it often seemed that a floral bouquet was gliding along the avenues.

The feminine partners, thus displayed, had been chosen by these gallants for their loveliness. They were hatless, their black hair piled up over tortoiseshell combs draped with short mantillas. In their hair they wore, provocatively, red and white carnations, their dark vivid Spanish beauty offset by these flowers and billowing dresses. They passed slender arms around the waists of their young escorts. The posture of the riders was very erect as they proudly seated their superb horses.

It was a wonderful scene, a parade of handsome young men, lovely girls, costumes, horses, liveries and harnesses. Bevies of lustrous-eyed señoritas drove by in the low open carriages, their dresses cascading over the hoods and wheels. Up and down, turning, pausing for conversation, or to drink at one of the bright *casetas*, the procession continued from noon until three o'clock. Then the avenues emptied. The siesta followed. At ten o'clock, in a fairground ablaze with lanterns, music sounding from every *caseta*, the carnival would begin, and the dancing go on until dawn.

It was Miles Callender who suggested to Mary that he should fetch her for the evening carnival. He had cards for *casetas* where there would be Spanish dancing. Earlier in the afternoon he had been to a bull-fight in the great arena.

"A wonderful spectacle, but, oh, what a revolting exhibition! The bull's doomed to be dead within twenty minutes of coming into the arena," said Callender, as they drove to the fair. "I was in Alba's box. I don't think he really likes it, but as a great Spaniard he has to show himself. What beats me is how Spanish girls can stand seeing those grand bulls bled by picadors and tormented by the banderilleros. I must say my sympathy was with the bull. I was hoping all the time he'd get a matador! He'd no chance today. The great Montes was performing. The spectacle, of course, was superb —the tiers of faces, the sun sinking, leaving one half of the arena in shadow, and the *paseo* when the matadors marched in procession across the arena. They came right up to Jimmy's box and saluted him. There are two odd English-women in the house party. They were in the box this after-noon. They come from Lisbon; they're mad on bull-fighting, and travel all over Spain to see it. They know the names and histories of all the matadors. They admit the atrocious cruelty to those old horses, gored to death. But, dash it, one of 'em said she enjoyed cruelty! What do you think of that? I could see her sitting in the Colosseum turning her thumb down for the death of a gladiator. The pair of 'em have large white fans on which they've got the autographs of famous mata-dors. Revolting, I call it!"

Miles Callender's voice had passion in it and she loved him for it.

"I can't imagine Jimmy turning his thumb down. He's so gentle," observed Mary.

"Nor I. He's a charming fellow. Do you know what he said last night? He'd prefer a seat in the House of Lords to his in the President's box! Bad luck for him! As Duke of Berwick he's attainted in England. He says that, legally, now he's succeeded—he went to school in England—he's liable to be arrested for high treason and beheaded on Tower Hill! I can't see young Jimmy coming to that end! Let's go to his *caseta* first."

They found the *caseta* crowded with guests, though the house party had not yet arrived from a dinner at the Duke of Medinaceli's. It was already eleven o'clock.

"I expect they're just sitting down to dinner. I can never get accustomed to the late hours here in Seville. We often go in to dinner at ten," said Mary.

"Then you aren't visiting here?" asked Callender.

"Oh no! I'm almost a native! I came to work here over a year ago."

"Work? I can't imagine you working!"

"Why not?"

"Well—well, you're too pretty for any kind of office job," said Callender, a little embarrassed.

"I'm not in an office. I'm a governess, a very humble little governess in an Anglo-Spanish family."

"Lucky kids! Who are they?"

"I'm with Mr. Harcourt's family. He's a director of the Seville Waterworks Company, and the Rio Tinto Mines, English concerns here. His wife's Spanish. They have two children whom I'm preparing for a preparatory school in England. That's all my history!" said Mary gaily, as they found two chairs vacant among those surrounding the wooden dancing floor. Four couples were dancing the *Sevillanas* with great gusto. The young women's skirts flowed out as they turned before their flushed partners.

"Now I'll tell you who I am! Lieutenant Miles Callender, Royal Navy, aged twenty-five. Son of a poor widow, born in Esher, Surrey, educated at Dartmouth, now assistant Naval Attaché, British Embassy, Madrid," he said. "Can you dance a *Sevillana* like those couples?"

"Yes—can you?" asked Mary.

"Gosh, no!"

"Will you try with me?"

He looked at her, a little surprised.

"I'll try anything with you," he said, his fair face lit with a smile. "But I'll make a fool of myself!"

"No one will notice. Come on!" said Mary.

She caught him by the hand. The guitars started a new dance. The floor was full, the rattle of castanets and stamping of feet rose above the guitars. She took Callender firmly by the hand and went on to the wooden floor. He gave himself up to the surging movement, the staccato vivacity of the heady music. They flung themselves headlong into the group of swirling dancers. After ten minutes, utterly exhausted, his chestnut curls down over his brow, he cried for mercy. Mary led him off the floor. His eyes shone with admiration.

"But you're a positive Spaniard—you're marvellous!" he said, looking into her eyes. How fair, how fresh she was among these dark señoritas. They were lovely with their Andalusian eyes, their black arched eyebrows, long lashes, red lips and lustrous black hair emphasising the ivory pallor of their faces. But here was a girl with the dew of England on her—a scented rose. Her mouth was exquisite and her smile pierced him with its maiden beauty.

A professional quartette, with their own accompanists, going from *caseta* to *caseta*, gipsies from Triana across the river, lithe and swarthy, now took the floor. A wilder note sounded out of Moorish Spain, out of Africa. They danced with astonishing abandon in a rhythm that stirred the blood. Their finale, a tempestuous rondo, brought a storm of applause. With flashing eyes and teeth the lithe young gipsies went round with the hat, the girls distributed the red camelias from above their ears.

Then a young man stepped on to the floor alone, narrow-hipped, serpentine. He began to stamp with varied rhythms and crescendos. He twisted, he spun to the staccato hand-clapping and the clicking of castanets. He expressed passion, despair, arrogance, valour, all the varied themes of a lover—encouraged, repulsed, triumphant. *Olé Olé Corre!* shouted the guests. He left the floor. A gipsy youth began to sing the *Cante Flamenco* with their African cadenza, quarter-tones, high notes and a wild improvisatore ending, with throat throbbing and eyes flashing under his fallen black hair. He ended in a storm of applause. *Olé! Olé! Olé!* they shouted.

Footmen in the Alba liveries went round with trays of crystal glasses filled with *manzanilla*, a sherry-wine. There was a smell of food cooking.

"I believe we're going to have a beano at midnight," said

Callender. "What about a walk down the avenues to look at the other *casetas*? I've tickets for five. We'll be back before Jimmy arrives."

"I'd love it—it's very hot in here."

They left the *caseta* and joined the crowds in the avenues, walking under the long lines of red and orange lanterns. On every side there was the sound of guitars, castanets and the rhythm of heels stamping in the *Sevillana* dances. The *casetas* blazed with lights.

After they had walked down two avenues in the scented soft air, "Let's have a drive!" cried Callender, hailing an open carriage with a pair of horses. He gave the coachman an order, and the man, knowing the ways of lovers, turned off the lighted avenues, down a small road that soon grew dusky, the music faintly heard. The clop-clop of the horses' hooves sounded a quieter rhythm on the tarmac. They came to an avenue of eucalyptus trees.

"Your Spanish is quite good," said Mary, after he had exchanged a few sentences with the coachman about some steamer lights floating down the Guadalquivir River.

"Oh, no—it's very poor. I've just got a little patter," he said. "Not at all like your Spanish."

"But you've never heard mine!"

"Oh, yes, I have. You were talking to a little fat-cheeked escort you had on your left for supper at the ball. I listened in and couldn't get a word. You never saw me, dumb on your other side."

"Sorry—that was Díaz de Alcantara—the finest horseman in Spain," said Mary.

"I would cheerfully ride him down."

They laughed together, then a silence fell, only the hooves of the horses echoing in the avenue high-arched with eucalyptus branches. Somehow, on the carriage seat, his hand found hers. He felt a warm responding pressure. Neither spoke, they drove on in silence. He was aware of the arch of her neck, the white shoulders partly hidden by the crimson

Spanish shawl that draped them. He felt a great ache in his heart, and a dumbness seizing him.

"Will you call me Miles?" he asked at last.

"Yes, Miles," she responded, smiling at him.

"Mary, I can call you Mary?" he asked.

"Of course!"

He wanted to take her in his arms, with the aid of the old coachman who always spoke without turning round, and did not appear to know he had anyone in his carriage. But Miles had fear of a good fortune that seemed too great. He kept her hand while they drove on. Presently there was a new sound, in the dark woods above which a crescent moon had risen. There was a long low trill.

"A nightingale!" said Mary. "Listen!"

The trill came again out of the night, ascending this time.

"How lovely!" whispered Mary, with shining eyes.

Her beauty in the moonlight caught his breath.

"How lovely!" he echoed. Then he leaned forward and she seemed to be suddenly near him, so that their lips met. His arm was about her instantly and she felt him tremble as he held her. She turned her face upwards to his, but they hardly saw each other in the intensity of the moment. The nightingale sang unheard, the carriage moved forward but not in any world they had ever known. They were children in the enchanted wood.

III

They had three more days. Miles Callender was in and out of the Harcourts' house. They were delighted with the romance. The young Duke of Alba, amid a crowd of merry guests staying with him for the whole week of the *Feria*, never failed to include Mary in the endless parties.

There was no sleep for anyone in Seville that week. After dining in a Spanish friend's house they would turn homewards about three in the morning. Their way often led them through little *plazoletas* with orange trees, down narrow *calles* with high snow-white houses bathed in moonlight. Again and again as they wandered, the revolving vane on the high Giralda tower, with its figure of Faith holding the banner of Constantine, would come into view. Under old walls, purple with bougainvillea, or balconies tumbling with roses, there would be a sound of laughter and a lilt of guitars that would fade as young feet hurried over the cobbles. This was still the city known to the Phœnicians, the Carthaginians, the Romans, Goths and Moors. Here in poverty and neglect stout Córtez, the conqueror of Mexico, who had wrested from Montezuma the great Aztec kingdom, had ended his days. Christopher Columbus had eaten out his heart here. The youthful Velasquez had first tried his palette here, and also Murillo, with his cascades of cherubs. Along these narrow streets by night and dawn had flitted Don Juan and Figaro, the Barber of Seville, and Carmen, ghosts still moving to the music of Mozart, Rossini and Bizet.

And now it was, briefly, the Seville of Mary and Miles. They danced through the warm nights and drove home in the first light of dawn. There were the splendid entertainments in the Palacio de las Dueñas, and the Duchess of Medinaceli's Casa Pilatus. One morning they rode across the river to Triana to see the *feria de los gitanos*, the gipsies' cattle fair. A vast crowd was haggling over horses and cattle, amid a tangle of gipsies, wagons and carts, where they camped in indescribable disorder. Handsome, bold, they offered their horses, copers to a man, with brilliant eyes and swarthy smiles.

Once in the early morning they cantered down the *Paseo de las Delices*. The early fresh scent of roses filled the air, the birds sang in the tall trees, the gold light of dawn lit the old Guadalquivir River that had seen the Roman and Moorish galleons. Scarlet and white oleander bushes, camelia, juniper, myrtle, lime, eucalyptus and orange trees lined the avenues. They breakfasted in a little restaurant set in a rose-garden where fountains sparkled in the early sunlight.

The last day came. Miles Callender had to return to his

post. In three months he would be back again. Of course, Mary would come to Madrid?

"But I know no one there—and I have my work."

"Mrs. Harcourt will spare you—and I'll get Jimmy to ask you to one of his house parties in his wonderful Liria Palace," he replied impetuously. "What a pity Seville's such a long journey from Madrid!"

After he had left they exchanged letters regularly. In the next eight months he returned twice to Seville. It was during his last visit, when he was the Christmas guest of the Harcourts, that he asked her to marry him. He chose the moment when they were sitting in the water-garden of the old Alcázar where the young King Alfonso was spending a few days. Birds were singing in the warm winter sunshine. The air had the softness of spring.

"I have something I must tell you, before I give you my answer, Miles," she said, her hands nervously playing with her purse. "My father was sentenced to five years' penal servitude for embezzlement. He committed suicide as he left the dock. We were utterly bankrupt, my young brother went to Canada, and after a time these darling Harcourts, who had known my father, brought me here as a governess, a post that will end soon. You have your official career to think of. It might be a serious handicap. You must carefully consider this before you ask me to marry you. At the time it all happened, the young man to whom I was engaged, though it had not been announced, couldn't face it. I quite understood his position."

Miles turned on the bench where they sat side by side and placed both hands over hers as he looked into her eyes.

"My dear girl, you are telling me nothing I don't know— I've heard all this from almost the first day we met, and it means nothing to me. No, it means much—that I must look after you and cherish you!"

His low voice rang with a tender sincerity. He saw the tears hovering as she raised her face.

"You knew! And all this time I had believed you did not know. I've put off this dreadful confession," she said, her voice breaking. "I feared I would lose you—I didn't want to lose you, Miles. I love you deeply."

"I should have spoken before—but I was afraid of opening a wound. Some time after you came to Alba's we were breakfasting in the loggia overlooking the patio. There was a gossipy old Englishwoman, a friend of Alba's mother, in the house party. I heard her say to another woman: 'How pretty that Miss Bostowell is. Poor child, her father committed suicide after being sentenced for fraud, and she's earning her living as a governess.' I felt an even deeper attraction from that moment. I felt you had courage and wonderful poise after an ordeal that would have crushed most girls. Oddly enough, I know Cyril Ransome; we were *en poste* together for a short time in Brussels. He's a poor fish. He's just married a rich American girl who treats him like an office-boy."

"I'd heard of his marriage. Poor Cyril," commented Mary.

"And because of poor Cyril, lucky Miles!"

He leaned forward to take her in his arms and kiss her.

"Miles!" she protested, looking around.

"I don't care if King Alfonso walks in on us! I am going to the top of the Giralda tower and shout the great news all over Seville!" he cried, taking her.

IV

They were married the following October, on a warm autumnal day at the British Consulate in Madrid. The whole Harcourt family came up from Seville for the ceremony. The reception was held in the magnificent Palacio de Liria which the Duke of Alba placed at their disposal. Five hundred English, Spanish and American guests ascended the great staircase with its famous collection of works by Rubens, Van Dyck, Credi, Velasquez, Bellini, El Greco, including the family portraits, a Winterhalter of Alba's great-aunt, the

Empress Eugénie surrounded by the ladies of her court, the Titian of the Great Duke of Alva, and of his Stuart ancestor, James Fitzjames, Marshal of France, on whom his father James II conferred the dukedom of Berwick. Like a delighted boy, Alba piloted the wedding guests through the great salons. There were letters in cases from Bonnie Prince Charlie, pictures of the Pretender, and his brother the Cardinal Henry, Duke of York, Christopher Columbus's list of gold of the Indies sold in Burgos, and of the privileges given him by Ferdinand and Isabella. The banquet tables were offset in the grand salon by the Gobelin tapestries of *The Loves of the Gods*, to which Henry Harcourt, proposing the health of the bride and bridegroom, made happy reference.

The honeymoon was spent at a villa at Pollensa, in Majorca, lent to them, and here Mary's aunt, Mrs. Cavan, unable through illness to go to Madrid, came and spent a few days with them. There was only one note of sadness for Mary in all this, the leaving of the kind Harcourts and her farewell to her charges Philip and Isabel, soon leaving for school in England.

It was not expected that Miles Callender would be much longer *en poste* in Madrid, but they had found a small furnished apartment, with a balcony overlooking the gardens of the Buen Retiro. Here they settled.

Early in January Miles received news of the death of his mother, by which he became the owner of a small cottage in Oxfordshire. It grieved him that she died just before he could send her his great news, that Mary was expecting a baby.

The great event now stirring Madrid was the forthcoming marriage of the young King Alfonso, a dashing youth who had caught the public fancy in England, with the beautiful Princess Victoria Eugénie of Battenberg, a niece of King Edward VII. The bride was eighteen, the bridegroom twenty. The Press and the gossips had been marrying him for a long time. "Well, Señor, and to whom have they married me this morning?" he asked one of his gentlemen. But now he had made his choice, and it was said to be a real love match. The whole world was agog.

By good luck Miles Callender, who had had notice of recall to the active list and been posted to Chatham, was able to stay on for the great wedding. Madrid was a sea of banners flowing from scarlet and yellow Venetian masts. Not a detail went unheralded. Following the old Spanish custom, the bridegroom presented the bridal dress to his bride. It took forty women fifty-six days to make the Louis Seize costume, in white satin and cloth of silver, embroidered with small fleurs-de-lis, the Bourbon emblem. A mantle in Watteau pleats fell from the shoulders.

A week before the great day not a room was to be had in all Madrid. The royalties had arrived from all over the world. The Prince and Princess of Wales were at the Royal Palace, with the Infantas. Princess Frederick of Hanover and Prince Henry of Prussia were in the great house-party at the Palacio de Liria. The prices of seats along the route of the procession rose to astronomical figures. Miles and Mary were in great luck. A colleague at the Embassy had a second-floor apartment with a balcony at the end of the Calle Mayor, down which the marriage procession would pass on its return to the Royal Palace from the Church of San Jeronimo.

The great day arrived, Thursday, May 31st, a perfect day of sunshine, not too hot. Early in the morning, before the closing of the avenues, Mary and her husband hurried to their host's apartment, along streets ablaze with Spanish and English flags and high triumphal arches made of roses massed in the national colours, red, yellow and white, with blue petunias. The great houses along the processional route had hung their valuable tapestries over the balconies. The streets were lined with soldiers holding back the crowds.

The first note of excitement was struck by the departure of the royalties for the Church of San Jeronimo. The King's procession began with an aide-de-camp on horseback leading a body of mounted trumpeters and equerries, and with a cavalcade of twenty horsemen from the Spanish regiments. Their uniforms blazed in the morning sunlight. Two companies of English cavalry accompanied them, the 16th Lancers. Then followed the ornate coaches of the grandees of Spain drawn by plumed and caparisoned horses, with postilions and footmen in medieval costumes, each wearing the colours of the noble houses they represented. There were thirty of these coaches.

"There's the Duke of Alba!" shouted Miles. He waved frantically, and the little group of guests cheered. He must have heard them, for he looked out of his state coach and waved a hand. When the grandees had gone, the royal carriages came up, the Bronze landau with the King-of-Arms and the Chief Huntsmen, and then another landau with the Mistress of the Robes and the Commandant-General of the Halberdiers, a courtly old grandee with whom Mary had danced the previous evening at the Liria Palace. Next came the State carriages amid mounting excitement.

The boy Infante, Don Alfonso of Orleans, drove by, accompanied by the young Princes Rainier and Philip of Bourbon-Sicily. Their carriage brought the most cheering. Then came the two Infantas, Doña Paz and Doña Eulalia. They were followed by two more Infantas of Spain, Doña Maria Teresa and Doña Isabel, accompanied by Prince Gennaro of Bourbon, in a sky-blue uniform. Then came the German cortège, Prince Frederick of Hanover, Prince and Princess Alexander of Teck, Prince Henry of Prussia, the Duchess of Saxe-Coburg, Princess Beatrice of Saxe-Coburg, followed, in the Amaranth stagecoach with four horses, by Prince Eugene of Sweden, the Princes Louis and Alphonse of Bavaria with the Prince of Monaco.

"All the *Almanac de Gotha*!" cried young Loraine, their host.

"And the best is yet to be!" added Miles. "Look!"

The crimson and yellow Cipher coach came into view holding the Duke and Duchess of Genoa, Prince Albert of Prussia, in a maroon Uhlan uniform, and Prince Andrew of

Greece, in white and gold with a blue sash. The Tortoiseshell coach came next, with the Archduke Francis Ferdinand
of Austria. He sat with the Crown Prince Manoel of Portugal, Prince Albert of Belgium and the Grand Duke Vladimir
of Russia, all blazing with Orders. A Gala carriage raised
the cheering to new heights. In it sat, unaccompanied, the
Prince and Princess of Wales, the latter the flower of regality.
Then after a lull, the crowd in full voice hailed the Crown
coach and in it the young King, the bridegroom, with the
Infantes Don Carlos and his nephew, the Prince of Asturias,
Heir Presumptive. A mounted regiment brought up the rear.

They did not see the bride's procession, which had started
from the Ministry of Marine, and followed on after the
groom's procession had almost reached the church.

There was a pause now. The balconies emptied while the
guests chatted and took refreshment in the cool salons. The
crowds stolidly waited in the growing heat of the day. A few
minutes before noon the sound of saluting cannon told
Madrid that the royal procession had started from the
church for the Royal Palace, the wedding ceremony concluded. The balconies filled up again, and the growing roar
of the multitude announced its approach. It came at last, a
glittering pageant of carriages, horses, soldiers and footmen.
The royal carriages were in the same order. They came
slowly on, the coach of the Ducal Crown, the Amaranth
coach, the Cipher coach, the Tortoiseshell coach, the open
Gala carriage of the Prince and Princess of Wales, the
Mahogany coach with the Queen-Mother, Princess Henry
of Battenberg, and the two Infantas, then the Coach of the
Gold Panels, empty as if to increase expectancy, and finally,
the great Crown coach with the young King and Queen
smiling and acknowledging the wild cheering of the crowd.

It was a gala of coaches and carriages passing down the
Calle Mayor to which the grandees of Spain contributed
their own fabulous history. Among the most notable of the
equipages was that of the Duke of Alba, with its yellow

liveries. Notable also were the green coach of the Duchess
Fernán-Nuñez, the coach of the Duchess of Bailen, with its
blue and scarlet wheels and liveries, and of the Duke of
Aliaga, with scarlet wheels and gold harness, the horses
carrying red and yellow plumes. The Duke of Sotomeyer,
chief of the Royal Household, had a gilt carriage with blue
and red wheels. It was surpassed by the Marquis of Viana's
seventeenth-century carriage with painted panels. All the
grandeur and pride of the haughtiest aristocracy in the world
were here paraded, but the height of splendour was reached
when the Crown coach came into view. Sacred to the Royal
Family of Spain, it proclaimed the proud dynasty that had
ruled in the Old and New Worlds. On its panels were em-
blazoned the royal arms of Naples and Spain. Two golden
globes carried the royal crown. It was drawn by eight
magnificent horses, their heads adorned with white plumes,
their harness metalled with gold. As it came slowly into view,
there were tears in the eyes of many who saw its romantic
splendour set off by the youth of its royal occupants.

They were drawing near to the Royal Palace now, with
only a few yards to go before turning by the cathedral. They
had passed the crowded balconies of the Ayuntamiento, the
Town Hall, its stands crammed with civil dignities, they
came almost to the small plaza of the Church of Santa Maria,
where there was a brief pause in the last part of the Calle
Mayor while the long procession ahead spaced itself.

Suddenly, by the headquarters of the Captain-General of
Madrid, there was a vivid flash of flame and a tremendous
report. Someone from a balcony in the Calle Mayor had
thrown a bouquet. Hidden in it was a bomb whose detona-
tion shook the street.

No one ever recalled clearly the ghastly details of this
diabolical deed. The bomb had been skilfully thrown. It
exploded between the front of the Crown coach, splintering
it, and the hindmost pair of horses, annihilating them. The
explosion was terrific. Instantly there was a stampede of

terrified, bleeding horses, a surging of the crowds in panic, but all this was hidden by a dense cloud of acrid smoke that cloaked the scene of carnage. As the smoke lifted the dying and wounded lay around, deluged in their own blood and that of the mangled horses.

Mary and Miles, on the balcony with its crowd of guests, never quite comprehended the ghastly spectacle. They saw, as the smoke cleared, the young King and his bride in the splintered coach, apparently uninjured. The equerries rushed towards them. The King coolly handed down his trembling Queen, and then took her in his arms. He had been hit by a bomb splinter, but the medal of a decoration had saved him. The bride's white silk wedding gown was crimsoned with the blood of the carriage horses. Her satin shoes stained, she stood in a morass of mangled flesh. The grooms fought madly to hold the terrified horses that had broken from their traces. A mounted equerry lay dying in the gutter and half a dozen bodies of spectators made little black heaps in the roadway. Panic broke out on the grandstands along the street.

"It is nothing, let us go on," said the young King, holding his bride, as the equerries came up.

But the procession could not go on. Dead horses, bodies, and a shattered coach blocked the way. Don Carlos of Bourbon ran up, excited. The King calmed him. "Bring the Carriage of Respect—and let us go on," he commanded. He half-turned to the Queen as it came up so that she might not see the spectacle of the dead and the dying, but she had seen it, and was splashed with blood.

They mounted the new coach. The King helped in his bride amid a crowd of officials, all in deep silence. His voice was heard as he seated himself, saying, "Drive slowly to the Palace."

The coach moved on. Turning the corner of the Calle, the cheering broke out again, evoked by a spectacle of calm courage amid terror.

Mary, in the front row on the balcony, had been stunned

by the explosion. Petrified, she clutched the draped balustrade, and stood there until the acrid smoke lifted, when the atrocious scene below was displayed. Suddenly she was aware of Miles behind, speaking to her, his hands on her waist, as other occupants pressed by them to reach the salon. Choking with the fumes, she tried to answer him, then felt him guide her into the salon.

"Oh, my dear," said a woman, seeing her eyes wide-open with horror. She came forward and Mary saw what she had seen. Her bodice was bespattered with blood. From her bare neck the woman removed a piece of livid flesh thrown up from the street. At that moment Miles felt his wife collapse. They carried her into a small salon where three other guests who had fainted had also been taken.

v

The bomb outrage shocked the world. There was a cloud over all the festivities in Madrid that night, over the banquets and balls in the Royal Palace and the residences of the grandees. They talked in hushed voices of the blood-splashed bride whose wedding day had been ruined. They applauded the composure of the young King within a few minutes of the attempted assassination, so that those who had already gained the palace, and awaited the royal couple by the grand staircase, were mostly unaware of the recent tragedy, until they were shocked by the spectacle of the young Queen with her bloodstained shoes and train. Her ladies-in-waiting hurried her away.

The next day Madrid rang with the story of a superb gesture. Towards midnight the royal couple entered an open carriage and for almost two hours drove round the illuminated capital, to the tumultuous cheering of the Madrileños, as though nothing had marred the bridal day.

Despite the shock she had suffered, Mary Callender went to the ball given for five hundred guests in the great palace of the Duke of Medinaceli. It was dawn when the carriage took them home. Miles had done his utmost to persuade Mary to stay at home.

"But what if we all stay at home, Miles? Every party will be ruined, and the trouble and expense they have all gone to! I'm quite all right, really, darling!"

She had a new dress for the ball, cream satin with silver spangles which the dressmaker had skilfully made in order to disguise that she was pregnant.

It was their last Spanish ball. Three weeks later on a hot June day they arrived in London. They proceeded after a few days to the cottage Miles had inherited from his mother, at Easter Common, a few miles out of Henley-on-Thames. After a short time at Chatham, Miles expected to be appointed to a ship. Mary's baby was due in August and her Aunt Helen was coming from Majorca to stay with her.

CHAPTER VI

I

ON the third of August, at five o'clock in the summer dawn, Mary gave birth to a son. It was not an easy delivery and when her husband, who had come post-haste from Chatham, saw her, his elation over the event which had given him a son and heir quickly collapsed. For two days he never left her side. Her recovery was slow.

He had a shock when he saw the baby held in its mother's arms. It seemed a shapeless lump of fretful boiled flesh, and he was startled when Mrs. Cavan said—"That's probably how you looked."

"And now look at me! Miracles never cease!" he cried jocularly. "Well, let's hope he takes after his mother, then he'll be something!"

He stooped and kissed Mary, and rubbed his hand over the baby's head with its fuzz of hair.

"I believe the little beggar's going to be ginger! We've an awful lot of redheads in our family," said Miles.

"I think you are very uncomplimentary to a future admiral," said Mary's aunt.

"A future Admiral of the Fleet, and Knight Commander of the Bath—something to put his old dad in the shade! Good-bye, darling—back in a week," he said, giving his wife a hug that took in the baby, and was gone.

About two months later, when Miles Callender returned on one of his periodic visits, Mrs. Cavan took him aside at her first opportunity.

"Dr. Jones wants you to call him—he would like to see you at his surgery. He'd rather Mary didn't know. He doesn't want to alarm her," she said.

"Good God! There's nothing wrong with Mary?" cried

Miles. "She looks blooming! I'm arranging for a christening in the Naval Chapel at Chatham. I thought we'd induct Christopher at once. We're going to have quite a party. The Admiral's wife wants to give a lunch," he said, unpacking his week-end bag in the low, black-raftered bedroom where Mrs. Cavan had caught him alone.

"It's not Mary—she's quite well, Miles."

"Christopher?—there's nothing wrong, is there?" he asked apprehensively. "Mary's not said anything?"

"No—but I think she's a little worried. Don't say anything to her, and go and see Dr. Jones without letting her know."

"You scare me!" he said, standing up straight and brushing his hair back nervously. His head almost touched the ceiling of the Elizabethan cottage.

"Oh, it may be just a little thing," said Mrs. Cavan reassuringly, leaving the room.

He washed, brushed his hair and put away his things. He placed his pyjamas at the side of Mary's silk nightdress case on the large double bed. Christopher's cot was over by the long low window overlooking the orchard. He rarely disturbed them, he was a good kid.

He motored in to Henley. It was easy to get away, the car required a new headlight bulb. While they were putting it in, he walked down the street to Dr. Jones's surgery. He lived in a beautiful old Georgian house, with a colonnaded portico painted white. The surgery was in a wing of the house, fronting a long back garden, with a lawn running like a green carpet between two herbaceous beds. It was not patients' visiting-hours, he saw by the brass plate, but he took a chance and rang the bell.

The door was opened not by the maid but by Dr. Jones himself.

"Oh, my dear Callender! You're just the fellow I want to see!" he cried jovially. He had a bunch of roses in his hand and wore leather gardening gloves. "Just cut 'em. What do you think of these? Aren't they beautiful? *The Reverend*

William Ewbank. I wonder who he was; some old vicar with a passion for roses, I suppose. That's the kind of immortality I'd like, to look beautiful and smell sweet down the years!"

He led the way through the surgery into a small den.

"Mrs. Jones's up north, so I'm pigging it here," he said, indicating a table littered with odds and ends. "Sit down—you're not in any hurry?"

"No—Mary's aunt said you wanted to see me?"

"Ah, yes," said the doctor, offering a jar of tobacco to Miles. "Pipe or cigarette?"

"Cigarette, thank you."

He took a cigarette from a proffered case. The doctor slowly packed down the tobacco in his pipe. He lit it with deliberation, drew at it, and expelled the smoke.

"What I wanted to say to you—and not to Mrs. Callender at this stage—is that I would be happier if I might call in a specialist to have a look at the baby," he said quietly.

His eyes met Miles's, and he saw the quick apprehension in them.

"There's something that worries me a little. You don't mind if I ask you a question?" he continued. "Is there any history of—er—mental disturbance in your family or that of your wife?"

"Good Lord, no! My wife did have a terrible shock a few months before Christopher was born. We were in Madrid for the wedding of King Alfonso and Princess Victoria Eugénie of Battenberg. The balcony from which we watched the procession was exactly opposite the place where the bomb was thrown. We got the blast and my wife was splashed with blood. She collapsed afterwards."

"I don't think that would explain the symptoms I suspect. The delivery was, as you know, a very difficult one."

"It's—it's nothing mental?" asked Miles.

"We'll hope not. It's too early to say. It would be foolish of us to exaggerate the condition. I might be quite wrong, but, as I've said, I'd like to have the opinion of someone

L.T.—7*

better qualified than I am. Early symptoms can disappear in a healthy child."

"Or develop?" asked Miles anxiously.

"Or develop, but we'll hope not. Sir Henry Allbright is the specialist I have in mind, the best in Harley Street for juvenile nervous derangements. Do you wish me to consult with him?"

"Certainly," said Miles.

"Thank you. Now there's Mrs. Callender—I will leave it to you. We must not alarm her unduly. Happily she's not a highly strung woman."

"But what shall I tell her—there must be some sort of reason for calling in a specialist?" asked Miles.

Dr. Jones looked at his roses for a few moments. He was deeply distressed, but he resolutely controlled himself, and when he spoke neither his face nor his voice betrayed his apprehension.

"You can say I'm a little baffled by symptoms of nervous insensitivity, and would like someone of wider experience to give an opinion. Above all, don't give your wife cause for alarm, it may be quite unnecessary."

"Thank you. I'll do my best. When do you want us to see Sir Henry?"

"I'll put in a call this evening—one day next week?"

"Any day, the sooner the better," said Miles as they rose.

Dr. Jones accompanied the young man to the door. "My regards to Mrs. Callender—and don't worry!" he said in parting.

He watched Callender go down the drive. Then he closed the door. For a moment he stood in the hall, and for no reason at all tapped the barometer, but was unaware whether it was Set Fair or Stormy. A general practitioner of forty years' standing, he had seen many tragedies. This was one of the worst. He knew that the Callender child was a mongol idiot.

II

The lives of Miles and Mary Callender might have been wrecked by the cruel stroke Fate had dealt them at the very beginning of their married life, but under the weight of their tragedy they were drawn even nearer to each other. They kept their sorrow within their own walls, the bond of a deep undefeatable love sustaining the burden they carried. They were aware of the sympathy that flowed out to them and any embarrassment in those who expressed sympathy vanished before their serenity.

Each year that passed emphasised the abnormality of their small son. He made uncouth sounds out of a distorted mouth. His uncontrollable legs could not support the misshapen body. The eyes betrayed the clouded mind that remained infantile. Yet the child's response to affection was unretarded. Any absence of his mother produced a profound agitation.

Young Christopher became Mary Callender's preoccupation. She nursed, bathed, fed and lavished affection upon the abnormal child of her womb. The Callenders found they could not trust any hired help, who soon became exasperated by her charge, and revolted by the services she must render, so the whole burden fell on Mary, clinging to the little cottage, dearer now for its remoteness from the world.

Miles Callender, appointed to a ship on the Mediterranean station, knew there was no possibility of moving out his family to Malta. Mary would not hear of it. Deeply sensitive, he did not really desire it himself. His sunny buoyant nature gradually grew grave and prepossessed. Once, when Christopher was almost eight, anguished by the burden Mary was sustaining, he suggested sending the boy to a home for defective children, under the pretence of seeking a cure. Mary's reaction was immediate and almost violent. It was the first time there had been any serious breach between them.

"How can you think of such a thing!" she cried indignantly. "Send Christopher to one of those terrible institutions! It would kill him—and me! You've not heard me complain? Who attends him, nurses him, feeds him? Have I ever failed in my duty? The idea is monstrous! Never! Never!" she cried with passion, and abruptly left the room.

He heard her go upstairs. Wretched, he followed and found her sobbing on their bed.

"Mary! Mary!" he said, bending down and taking her in his arms. "I'm sorry. Of course we'll never send Christopher away."

He was a lieutenant-commander now, and in the Home Fleet, with the First Destroyer Flotilla. In the middle of June, having some leave, they went for a month to a small house outside Cowes, lent to them by a brother officer. They took with them a maid, a sluggish but amiable creature who was kind to Christopher. There was a small jetty and a sailing-boat. Miles took Christopher down to the boat and put him on a mattress in the stern. He liked to look up and see the clouds pass over the speeding sail. He had never been able to speak properly, but he contrived to make inarticulate sounds by which he expressed himself and they understood him. The lolling of his head seemed more pathetic because of his mop of lovely chestnut curls. He was of a happy disposition, laughed easily and was deeply affectionate, with a baby's clinging attachment. There were odd moments when it was possible to see in him an attractive boy, but more often it was cruelly plain that he was a monster with a vacant mind. To Mary he was her whole existence. Miles experienced anguished moments when he wondered whether he was growing a little remote in her life, the child being its centre.

The weather at Cowes was glorious. They sailed, picnicked, and sat in the shade of a chestnut tree after lunch. Miles read the newspapers desultorily. Mary devoured them.

Christopher tumbled over the lawn wielding a fly-swatter. He had a passion for killing flies.

"Who's the Archduke Ferdinand—and how could he be the heir to the Austrian Empire?" asked Mary from a deck-chair, looking up from her paper.

"The Emperor Francis Joseph's got no son. The Crown Prince committed suicide at Mayerling, with his mistress Marie Vetsera. So the Archduke Francis Ferdinand, a nephew, will inherit the throne. Why do you ask? What's he doing?" asked Miles, half-asleep.

"He's doing nothing. He's dead. A Serbian student threw a bomb and killed him and his wife yesterday," replied Mary.

"Where?"

"In a place called Sarajevo, in Bosnia."

"That's awkward for old Francis Joseph! The Archduke married a commoner, a German-Czech. It was a morganatic marriage. The old man insisted on his nephew renouncing for his children all rights to the throne."

"They say there's a grave crisis between Austria and Serbia," said Mary, quoting. "Austria may send an ultimatum."

"There's always a grave crisis in those Balkans. Thank God, they've no navy worth mentioning, so they can't bother us," replied Miles, lighting his pipe.

The weather was halcyon. Christopher laughed, and wobbled about on the lawn. They made a discovery. One day Miles brought home a portable gramophone. The boy was enchanted by it. A look of utter happiness showed in his face as he listened to the music it produced. He wanted the records played again and again.

Their month was not out when Miles received a telegram recalling him to his ship.

"But why, you have another week's leave?" cried Mary.

"Things don't look too good. We're mobilising the Fleet —a precaution, I expect," replied Miles. "Germany's egging on Austria to be firm."

They packed hurriedly and returned to Easter Common the next morning. Miles said good-bye. He lifted Christopher up before he went out to the car. Some intuition of disaster possessed the child. He flung his arms round his father's neck and burst into tears. He had never shown such emotion on the many previous occasions when his father had departed.

"You take care of Mummy until I come back," said Miles, pinching his cheek.

Christopher's head wobbled and the uncouth sounds he made were an assurance that he would.

On August 4th England declared war on Germany. Miles came back to his home four times in the next twelve months. He was stationed in the farthest north of Great Britain, at Scapa Flow, with the Grand Fleet, in H.M.S. *Invincible*. In May, 1916, he went down with his ship in the Battle of Jutland. At the age of thirty-six Mary Callender was a widow with an imbecile son. Christopher was all she had left in the world.

Her love for the child grew even intenser. Now they were alone her whole life was centred upon his needs. They shut themselves up in the little house on the Chiltern Hills.

III

Three months after the loss of her husband Mary had a visitor. It was her brother, Henry Bostowell, a stalwart lad of twenty-four, a lieutenant in the Canadian Black Watch. He came on short leave while his regiment was training in England, before going to France. Though brother and sister were strangers and belonged to different worlds, there was a quickly affectionate reunion after long years. He spent his final leave at the cottage, a brave young figure in his dark green and blue kilt. He was adored by Christopher, with whom he played. Henry was shocked by the sight of his nephew and realised why Mary, who had corresponded with him, had never sent him a photograph of her child. But the moment he saw the boy he allowed neither revulsion nor pity to show in his manner.

Mary could see in Henry the likeness of her father. He was built in the same big way, easy and confident in manner, with the same resonant voice. His brief appearance left a deep impression on the quiet house. After six months in France, a week after his promotion to captain, he was killed. For a year Christopher enquired when Uncle Henry was coming back.

The attempt to teach Christopher his letters failed completely. He was a lively little boy. The children in the district were frightened by him, or contemptuous. Mary Callender, fearful that he might suffer ridicule, did not encourage them to come to the cottage.

Mother and son were soon forgotten by the world. Occasionally they would be seen walking across the Common, the boy dragging his legs as he hung on to his mother's arm, rolling his head and talking to her in his uncouth manner. As he grew older he became more ungainly, but in the merciful providence that makes a mother's love stronger by the claims laid upon it, Mary Callender's devotion steadily increased. A help, a young village woman, came in to do the rough work, but the task of tending Christopher was exclusively Mary's. She washed, dressed and fed him. Her small officer's widow's pension, with the increased cost of living, barely sufficed for their needs, but by exercising rigid economy she maintained a genteel state. She made most of Christopher's clothing and much of her own wardrobe, being a skilful needlewoman.

One day Philip Harcourt, the little boy she had taught in Seville, arrived in London. He was now a young man of twenty-four, engaged to an English girl. He wrote asking if he might motor down to see her and bring his fiancée. Her first instinct was to say that she was going to be away, her second to suggest meeting him in London. It was many years since she had heard from the Harcourts. The correspondent of the family, boisterous, kind Mr. Harcourt, was dead. Mary often wondered how much they knew. Possibly everything, but whatever they had learned it was a different matter for Philip Harcourt to see Christopher. Then, heartily ashamed of herself for what seemed an act of cowardice, she invited the young couple to lunch. The little boy she had taught was a six-foot swarthy young man, with all his mother's colouring and vivacity.

"This is Christopher," said Mary simply, when the boy came shuffling in and stared at the visitors, a little hostile.

They contrived to see nothing unusual in the boy who stood there with a head too big, slit eyes, high cheekbones that gave him a Mongolian cast, and arms and legs that had no co-ordination.

"How do you do, Christopher? How very nice to see you and your dear mama. This is my fiancée, Nancy."

He put out his hand, but the boy drew back suspiciously.

"Come, now, you're not afraid of Philip? He was the little boy I taught in Seville that I've told you about," said his mother encouragingly.

Philip Harcourt went forward and put his arm round the boy's shoulder. Christopher looked up, made some incomprehensible sounds, and then held out his hand to Nancy Canford.

Mrs. Callender and Philip exchanged glances. The whole tragedy of her life was revealed at once.

"One day your mother must bring you to Seville. We all loved her, she was full of fun, and beautiful," said Philip, hugging the boy. He had made a conquest.

That was early in 1920, Christopher was thirteen. It was now certain that he would never know a normal life, that always he would have to be nursed and watched. The neighbours all knew the tragic drama being played in Juniper Cottage. They offered their help, but Mrs. Callender made it plain that she preferred to be left alone. At forty her hair was already grey and her fresh loveliness had gone, but she was a notable woman with something arresting in her eyes, and a firm manner with a rather contradictory sweetness in her voice.

IV

In their first years at Juniper Cottage repeated efforts were made by people living in the district to draw Mary Callender into the active social life around, but there was always the problem of someone to look after Christopher. If she left him for half an hour he became distressed. There was a dreadful occasion when, accepting an invitation to lunch at Phyllis Court, in Henley-on-Thames, during the Regatta, she had arranged with a young woman, who came in twice a week to help her with the cleaning, to take charge of Christopher during her absence. It was the first time that she had ever left him. He was by now a tall youth of almost eighteen, the promise of a splendid manhood marred by the malice of Nature. He had beautiful hair, dark blond, and fine teeth. There were moments when, with his head turned so that his vacant eyes and twisted mouth were not visible, his profile had an arresting beauty. Except for very occasional rages, when he wildly waved his arms and bellowed like a wounded animal, he was sweet-tempered. His readiness to laugh and his loudness in doing so betrayed his mental condition. With the increasing years his affection deepened.

Later, Mary Callender wondered what had possessed her to desert Christopher on that beautiful July day in Regatta Week. He was puzzled and apprehensive but made no protest when she left.

"Ethel will look after you, and give you your lunch. I shall be back by four o'clock. Be a good boy, Christopher," said his mother.

"Je—je-je," he ejaculated, rolling his head, his hand clutching hers.

About noon the Andersons, her hosts, called in the car for her. They got out and talked with Christopher, who knew them. He ambled down to the garden gate and waved to them happily as the car went off, with the faithful Ethel, the jobbing gardener's young wife, peering out of the kitchen window. It was the first time in eighteen years that he had been separated from his mother.

"There, you see, Mrs. Callender, Christopher's quite happy. I'm sure you ought to get away at times. It'll make him much more independent," said Mrs. Anderson, sitting with her in the back of the car.

"I confess I feel uneasy. I've given Ethel the Club telephone number in case I'm wanted," said Mary Callender.

"You're the most wonderful mother in the world," cried Colonel Anderson over his shoulder as he drove. "But I think you should have a break occasionally. It'll be good for Christopher—after all, he's no longer a boy."

Mary Callender made no reply. They could never understand that her whole life had one single purpose, to protect Christopher, that her universe was bounded by the walls of the small cottage in which they lived for each other. She knew well the things that were said in the neighbourhood, that she was a martyr, that Christopher should be placed in an institution. They could never believe that what they considered bondage to an idiot boy was the richest, most rewarding thing in her life. She tried resolutely to dismiss the fear that haunted her—what would become of her poor son when she was no longer there to look after him. Now another fear began to trespass on her peace of mind. The small pension that she received as the widow of a naval officer became less and less adequate. The Great War had increased the cost of living. Her old aunt, still in Majorca, had also felt the pinch with the passing of years, and the small contribution she had made to her niece had now ceased. Old Mrs. Cavan could barely exist in her Sóller backwater.

When they had first come to Juniper Cottage they had had a maid. After Miles's death she had economised by having a

woman come in each day. Now she had the trustworthy
Ethel only two days a week. She was one of the few local
women who showed no aversion to Christopher, who ambled
around her and talked to her in his uncouth manner. She
pretended to understand him and treated him as a normal
intelligent person. Sometimes she brought with her a little
daughter of eight, and hand in hand the child would go out
on the Common with the tall ambling youth. He was skilled
at making daisy chains with which he delighted in crowning
the child. They also shared a delight in a Swiss musical-box
that Mrs. Cornish, the grocer's wife, had given him.

It was the Friday of Regatta Week and the wide lawns of
Phyllis Court, and the rose-covered river walk overlooking
the course, were crowded. Across the water a band played
gaily in the Stewards' Enclosure. They arrived in time for
the two last races of the morning programme. The Andersons
had a box on the top tier of the grandstand commanding a
view of the long shining river as far as Temple Island with
its background of the wooded Chiltern Hills. It was a sunny
day, the air warm, the scene brilliant with colour and
movement.

They were leaving their box and about to go down to the
Clubhouse for luncheon when Mary Callender heard her
name called by someone who had hurried up behind her.
She turned and found a swarthy-looking man, stout, elegantly dressed, in a light grey suit. He took off his Homburg
hat and, smiling behind large tortoiseshell glasses, extended
a hand towards her.

"Mary, after all these years!" he exclaimed.

She looked at him, puzzled for a moment. He was accompanied by two ladies, and a boy whose darkness was emphasised by his white jacket and shorts.

"But you know me—Mohamed Kafi? How nice to see
you!" he said.

Mary took his hand. The slender Mohamed Kafi had
vanished, but the eyes and smile of this rotund dark man

were the same. His hair was as black and curly as before, crowning a head that had lost its classical fineness.

"Let me introduce my wife and my hostess, Lady Mellingham—and this is my son."

They shook hands. Mary introduced the Andersons.

"How wonderful to see you here, Mary! We are staying with the Mellinghams at Taplow and they've brought us over. How are you and where are you living? I heard you had married."

She interrupted his eager questions.

"Yes, I'm now a widow—Mrs. Callender," said Mary.

"Oh, I'm sorry. Children, I hope?"

"One son."

"Ah, that's nice. I'm lucky too!" he exclaimed, putting his hand on the shoulder of the boy at his side, so obviously his son. "Well, now I hope we shall see much of each other. My wife and I will be delighted if you would come and dine with us in London."

"You're staying some time?" asked Mary as they moved towards the stairs.

"Oh, yes, for a time, I hope. I'm *en poste* at the Egyptian Embassy. To think we haven't seen each other since—since——"

"My father's tragedy," said Mary quietly.

"Yes, I was grieved by that."

"Thank you."

"Where can we find you?"

"I live at Juniper Cottage, Easter Common."

"What a delightful address!" He repeated it. "I shan't forget that. We're leaving after lunch. I'll write to you. We must meet again soon."

The party descended the stairs to the lawns and crossed to the Clubhouse, crowded with members seeking their tables. They parted. Kafi's wife was a handsome, heavily built woman with beautiful eyes. The boy, slender-legged, bright-eyed, was like a dark bird. The elder Kafi had renewed his glamorous youth.

"Did you see her carbochon clasps—worth a couple of thousand pounds at least!" exclaimed Mrs. Anderson, impressed. "Who are they?"

"Mohamed Kafi and his wife. I knew him in Cairo over twenty years ago," replied Mary. "He's a rich landowner who was very hospitable to us. He's now here with the Egyptian Embassy."

They were just finishing lunch when a pageboy, going from table to table, called Mary Callender's name.

"Yes? Mrs. Callender's here. What is it?" asked Colonel Anderson.

"The lady's wanted on the telephone, sir."

Mary jumped up, her face suddenly pale.

"Let me go to the telephone—you stay with Alice," he said, rising.

"It's Christopher!" cried Mary.

Mrs. Anderson caught her hand, pulling her down to her chair.

"Now don't worry, darling. George will deal with it, whatever it is," said Mrs. Anderson, soothingly.

In a few minutes Colonel Anderson came back to the table. He looked grave despite the confident manner he assumed.

"I think we should go back to the cottage. There's been a little upset with Christopher," he said gently.

"What is it? Tell me, please!" cried Mary.

"The boy got a little out of hand and frightened Ethel—but it's all right now."

"Out of hand? How? What happened?" asked Mary, white-faced with apprehension.

"I think we must wait—they didn't want to say much on the telephone," said Anderson as they left the table.

"Who called me?"

"Cornish, the grocer. Now don't worry. They've got Christopher quite safe and sound," said Anderson kindly.

In a few minutes they retrieved their car from the parking enclosure and were on their way to Easter Common.

V

Mary never forgot the nightmare of those next few hours. They called first at the little grocer's shop kept by the Cornishes, an amiable aged couple. Cornish must have been waiting for them. He came to the car as soon as it had stopped.

"Come right into the parlour, sir," he said to Colonel Anderson. "Everyone'll be gaping at us."

Mrs. Cornish met them in the little parlour behind the shop. She looked nervous and perturbed, but her husband was quite calm as he narrated what had happened.

"I was just delivering the groceries Mrs. Callender had ordered, and was getting out of my van opposite the gate of the cottage, when I heard someone screaming for help. It was Ethel Lovelock running like a wild thing down the path from the kitchen, with Mr. Christopher coming after her. I couldn't think what had happened. He was making the most awful sounds and looked quite out of himself. I stopped him, but he fought me like a young lion—he's surprisingly strong—and I couldn't hold him. He bit me on the hand"— he held up a bandaged left hand as he spoke—"and broke away from me and went off over the Common."

"Where is he?" asked Mary.

"Locked up. They got him later."

"Who?" asked Mrs. Anderson.

"I sent Murdock and Harris over the Common. They found him whimpering in a bush, but they had a great job to catch him and he struggled all the way home," replied Cornish.

"He's at the cottage?" asked Anderson.

"No, Colonel—he's locked up in Murdock's coalshed. They're real scared of him, and all the women, too."

"The women—why are they scared?" asked Mrs. Anderson. "He wouldn't hurt any woman!"

"That's just the trouble, ma'am. When we'd got Ethel calmed down we learned what had happened, though I'd guessed by the state of her clothes."

"What do you mean?" asked Anderson.

"Ethel was in the kitchen, sir, when Mr. Christopher comes in and stands looking at her in a funny way. Then he comes up to her and says something she can't understand. Before she could do anything he'd got hold of her and begun to tear at her bodice. She fought him off, but not before he'd messed her about and torn off half her bodice. It was at that moment as she got away that I came on the scene. He just went mad, sir. I'm afraid it's all over the village."

"Where is Ethel?" asked Mrs. Anderson.

"She's in her cottage. They sent for her husband. He's talking about calling for the police, but I've persuaded him to hold his hand until you come. He's a nice fellow, but naturally——"

"That's very thoughtful of you," said Anderson. "I'll go and see him at once. Is Christopher still locked up at Murdock's?"

"Yes, sir. They're real scared of him."

"I'll go to him when we've seen Ethel. It's all my fault. I should never have left him," said Mary.

Mrs. Anderson put her arm around her.

"You've been a most wonderful mother to the poor boy. You've nothing to reproach yourself for. Leave everything to George. We must go and get Christopher."

They thanked the Cornishes and went to the cottage where Ethel Lovelock lived. They found her calm, though suffering from shock. She told her story very simply. There was only one interpretation possible. It was a case of attempted rape on the part of the demented youth. Unlike his wife, Lovelock was indignant and bellicose. "He ain't safe to have around! He ought to have been put away long ago! I know what the police'll do!"

"Be quiet!" said his wife. "We aren't going to have no police in this! I'm making no charge."

"Thank you, Ethel," said Mary Callender.

Ethel Lovelock took the elder woman's hand in hers and pressed it. "I'm real sorry for you and poor Mr. Christopher. It was a shock, but I'll get over it. Won't you go and get him out of the shed. He must be real scared."

They found a cluster of gossips outside the Murdocks' gate.

"We've got him in there, sir. He hasn't made a sound since we put him in—but I'm really scared to go in. Surprising how strong he is!" commented Murdock. Mrs. Murdock and two children stood in the background, wide-eyed.

"I will go in to him," said Mary Callender quietly. "Take me to the shed."

The coalshed stood at the bottom of the garden. It was a low, sturdy wooden erection, with a single door, padlocked.

"We'd nowhere else to put him," said Murdock apologetically as he unlocked the door, and stood back warily.

Mary went forward. She could see nothing in the dark, cluttered-up shed.

"Christopher!" she called gently.

There was a movement at the back of the shed. Her son had risen from a heap of coal slack on which he had been lying. He stumbled forward into the light, an appalling apparition. His lip had been cut and the blood had run down his chin and throat. He had been crying and had smeared his face with blood and coal grime so that he presented a grotesque spectacle to the small group in the open air. He came out into the light, dazed, trembling. The moment that he saw his mother he rushed into her arms, laid his head on her shoulder and sobbed abandonedly. Without a word she led him towards the car. Ten minutes later they were back in Juniper Cottage. With the help of Mrs. Anderson, Mary washed him and put him to bed. He was quiet and exhausted.

CHAPTER VII

I

AFTER this event they were recluses from the world more than ever. The story of the attempted rape spread around the district. Christopher was an object to be feared. Mother and son were seen less often walking on the Common. They received no visitors except the doctor, the local vicar and the kind Andersons. Ethel succeeded in suppressing the action threatened by her husband, but he was firm in his refusal to let her go back to Juniper Cottage. It became impossible to get outside help. Mary Callender now did the whole of the domestic work. There was one benefit from this increased labour. Without any explanation, she could save the money she had paid to Ethel. Dr. Woodfall from Henley, their doctor since the death of Dr. Jones, a kind, overworked man, beloved throughout the countryside, came and discussed Christopher's case with her. Any suggestion that her son should be sent away met with a firm refusal.

"I feel I should warn you, Mrs. Callender, that Christopher may be increasingly difficult to deal with. He is now a youth of eighteen. There's all the adolescent sexual urge of a normal youth with only an infantile control. It would be unsafe to have any girl or young woman about the house, and he should never be allowed out alone."

"No one comes to the house. I allow no visitors to call," said Mary Callender. "Christopher never goes out of my sight. I blame myself bitterly for what happened. I failed in my duty to him by going to Phyllis Court. You need have no fears, Dr. Woodfall. This will never occur again."

The doctor looked at her. He knew she was a woman of strong will and her devotion aroused his admiration, but it seemed an unnatural burden for any woman to carry. She must have read his thoughts for her next remark was: "I have nobody in my life except my son. No one in the world would give him the love and care that I can give him. It's not a burden, as you may think. It's my whole life."

Dr. Woodfall said nothing more. Once a month during his rounds he paid a friendly call and Christopher became a great friend. On occasions the doctor took him out in his car. The youth obeyed him implicitly.

II

Two months after the incident at Juniper Cottage, while Christopher was seated in the garden enjoying the late September sunshine, he was excited by a large Rolls-Royce car slowing up at the gate. A man got out of it and as Christopher shuffled towards him asked if it was Juniper Cottage where Mrs. Callender lived.

Christopher, excited by the shining car, was more inarticulate than usual. His head wobbled, his mouth dripped with saliva, he vigorously pumped an arm up and down in his attempt to express himself. The stranger stared at the ungainly youth, embarrassed by the demonstration made before him. As he stood hesitantly just outside the rose-embowered gate, he saw a woman appear in the doorway up the garden path.

"Mary!" he called and advanced towards her, hat in hand.

She recognised the visitor at once. It was Mohamed Kafi, elegant in a dark blue suit. At a glance she took in the large automobile with a chauffeur at the wheel.

"Do you mind?" he asked, as he came up to her with outstretched hand. "I'm motoring to Oxford for lunch, and as I'm so near I thought I'd take the liberty of calling on you."

"It's very kind of you. Won't you come in?" said Mary, composedly, and turning, led him up into the little sitting-room that opened directly off the garden.

It was a pleasant room with a big bow-fronted window full of flowering plants. With its shining brasses over the high mantelpiece, its china ornaments, chintz-covered chairs, bookcase and large open fireplace with a log grate, it expressed comfort and daintiness.

"Do sit down. You see how simply we live," said Mary, seating herself. There was no sign of Christopher, he was examining the car and jabbering with the chauffeur.

"We." Kafi noticed the plural pronoun. He knew that she was the widow of a naval officer, with one son. Surely that idiot boy at the gate was not hers?

"We hardly had time to talk when we met at Phyllis Court," he said, "and I wanted to ask you so many things. I hesitated about calling since you did not reply to my letter —which you got?"

"Yes, I got it, Mohamed, thank you."

"Twenty-two years is a long time, Mary. You surely have forgiven me that little nonsense on our last excursion on the Nile?"

He smiled and twisted the gloves he was holding. She had placed a sherry decanter on the low oak table between them. He noticed how graceful she still was, her figure slim, her head beautiful, but he was shocked, as he had been on meeting her in July, by the impress of the years in her face and eyes. She had the withdrawn look of a woman who had passed through great suffering. Nothing of her early sparkle remained, only the voice came back from those memorable days in the Nile Valley. In exchange for the gaiety of her youth she had acquired an almost majestic presence, which he found a little forbidding. He observed that her eyes were as lovely as ever.

"You must think me rude in not replying to your letter, Mohamed," she said, filling two glasses with sherry. "I never leave this cottage. I've become a recluse. I can't accept any invitations." She looked at him calmly over the glasses as she spoke, and after a pause added, "But I'm glad to see you again. Egypt seems such a long way off, and has many happy memories for me."

"A very long way off," he echoed, raising the glass she gave him. "My dear Mary, we were all deeply distressed by the tragedy of your father, but you would have found nothing but sympathy if we could have seen you again. I heard you went to Spain, and married a young English naval officer. I'm sorry to hear he died. I've been more fortunate, I've three children. They're the treasure of my life. You met my elder boy."

"Yes. I've one son, Mohamed."

"Ah, that is good! Where is he, how old?"

"You've just seen him at the gate, my son Christopher," she said softly, looking at him.

He held the glass in his hand quite still but he felt his heart beat within him. So that frightful youth who had jibbered at him was her son! In a second he comprehended everything, her seclusion, her prematurely aged appearance, the aura of grave resignation visible in her manner. He could find no words for a few moments, and before he had framed some sort of response she had relieved him of the task.

"You'll understand why I never go out, why I left your letter unanswered. That very day I went to Henley Regatta and met you a frightful thing happened owing to my folly. I can never leave Christopher. I could not have one happy hour away from him. I love him deeply, he is all I have to live for. He's a very affectionate son."

"You live here alone, the two of you?"

"The two of us. We love the country. Now tell me something about yourself, Mohamed. How old are your children?"

He was relieved to talk of his family. He had been married fifteen years, just before his mother's death. He had three children, a girl and two boys.

"And your wife—an Egyptian, of course?"

"No, of Greek parents, born in Alexandria. She is four years younger than me."

"I hope you are very happy, Mohamed?"

He looked at her with his dark expressive eyes and made no comment.

"No?" asked Mary.

"Mama arranged my marriage. It was a good marriage. In Egypt we obey our mamas. My wife is beautiful, as you saw, but she is difficult. She is one of those women who knows everything and lets you know she knows."

"About you?" asked Mary, with a smile.

"About me, about all the universe. She's like a file."

"A file?"

"She wears one away by constant friction. Still I have my children, my lovely children," he said, with an air of resignation.

"And how many mistresses, Mohamed?" asked Mary frankly, a note of mischief in her voice.

"Ah, you haven't changed, *chérie. Toujours l'enfant terrible.* I will be honest—one only. But I only really loved once. It was you, Mary. Please don't smile, I am very serious. I would have married you and been most happy."

"Mohamed, you never asked me! And I don't think marriage was your intention the night you took me to hear the Colossus sing."

Mohamed Kafi raised his hands, then they both laughed.

"You would never take me seriously, *chérie*—but I loved you," he said. "I still love you, Mary."

"Thank you. You are still incorrigible, dear Mohamed."

"You've never forgiven me that episode in the Valley?"

"On the contrary, I recall it with much pleasure since I didn't lose my head," she replied.

"Perhaps, Mary, if you had lost it we should now recall it with more pleasure?"

His eyes laughed. She saw again the beguiling handsome libertine of that far-off moonlit night in Egypt.

"Tell me—Lalifu, does he still sing ravishingly?" she asked.

"Lalifu now teaches singing in New York. Oddly enough, he married a rich widow he met in Rome. Like all eunuchs, he's grown fat. I'm told his wife adores him. Some women are very strange."

"We are all very strange," said Mary. "No one can foresee——"

Her remark went unfinished. There was a noise at the door. A tall youth came forward with an ungainly gait.

"This is my son Christopher," said Mary, rising.

The youth stopped and looked at the brown-skinned man who had risen from his chair. His face became sullen as he surveyed him, head on one side.

"Christopher, this is Mr. Mohamed Kafi, an old friend of mine whom I knew when I was a girl in Egypt. Say 'How do you do' to Mr. Kafi," said his mother.

Christopher raised his hand waveringly but no sound came from his mouth. There was an awkward moment as they looked at each other, then Kafi put out his hand and took the youth's.

"Glad to know you, my boy. I see you've been looking at my car—you like cars?" asked Kafi.

Some kind of noise came from the wide-open mouth and a smile supplanted the frown. The youth had his mother's beautiful eyes. His head, but for the inane shaking, had a classical mould. The ghastly tragedy struck deeply into the Egyptian's heart. After a few moments of incomprehensible conversation, Kafi turned to Mary. Their eyes met. The whole drama of her lonely life was told without words.

"I must be going now. I'm due for lunch in Oxford at one o'clock. I'm very glad to have seen you, Mary," said Kafi, picking up his hat from the chair.

"It was very kind of you to come," she replied, going towards the door.

Kafi took the youth's limp hand and shook it. The same

idiot smile came back into the smooth face, handsome but for the loose hanging mouth and vacant eyes.

"Good-bye, young man. Take care of your mother," said Kafi, and went to the door.

Mary walked with him down the path to the rustic gate and out to the waiting car.

"Mary——" said Kafi, holding her hand between his own, as the chauffeur opened the door; but having pronounced her name he could find no words to add.

"You see why I do not go out, Mohamed. Christopher needs me," she said simply.

"Has he—was he always——?" stammered Kafi.

"From birth, poor darling," she replied, answering his unfinished question.

"And you are all alone? Hasn't the boy someone—an attendant? You can't be without help?"

"We get along very well. He's very affectionate and obedient. We are quite happy here."

"I hate saying good-bye. I may not see you again. My Party at home is losing office and there will be changes. I expect I'll soon be back in Cairo. Won't you come out and visit me—and bring Christopher? We could arrange something for him," said Kafi, still holding her hand.

"That's very kind of you, Mohamed, but you know it's impossible," said Mary.

They looked at each other in a brief silence.

"May I ask you one thing?" he said.

"Yes?"

"Don't be offended, but could I help in any way—financially, if necessary?"

She smiled at him and pressed his hand.

"That's very sweet of you, Mohamed. No, there's nothing you can do, thank you. I am quite all right," she answered.

"Then good-bye, Mary dear. I will write."

"Good-bye, Mohamed, and thank you for calling."

He got into the car, the chauffeur closed the door and

resumed his seat. They were slowly moving away when
Christopher came shuffling down the path, waving his arms
and attempting to shout a farewell. Mohamed put a hand
out of the window and waved in response. His last sight was
of Mary turning and putting a steadying arm around her
son at the gate.

III

Mary Callender was nearing fifty when the kidney trouble
that had afflicted her for some time became so acute that
Dr. Woodfall urged her to go into hospital for an operation.
She was adamant in her refusal. She would never allow herself to be taken away from Christopher.

For another year she suffered agony in an attempt to ward
off her illness. In the end, early in January, she consented to
be motored into Reading by Dr. Woodfall to see a specialist.
He gravely warned her that unless she had the operation
immediately she would be dead within a few months, or
earlier. As it was, there would be a grave risk with the
operation. She replied that she must consider the matter.

"I must warn you that every day's delay increases the risk
of the operation, Mrs. Callender. It should have been done
a year ago," said the specialist.

"You must give me forty-eight hours to make a decision,"
she said. "I have a son who needs my constant attention.
I can't go into hospital unless I know he will be seen to."

Dr. Woodfall brought her back to Juniper Cottage. He
impressed on her the urgency of her case and left her.

She had been obliged to ask Mrs. Cornish to look after
Christopher during her absence. This she did with the
greatest misgiving. Her last absence had resulted in a
tragedy. The grocer's wife had a heart of gold and had
agreed to come in for a few hours. She had singular success
in dealing with Christopher, now a young man of twenty-
four and increasingly helpless. He had to be waited upon
day and night. The shortest absence of his mother threw him

into a state of nervous terror. Mrs. Cornish, with her robust smile and cheerful manner, was the only other person he reposed any trust in.

"He's been very good all the time," said Mrs. Cornish, on Mary Callender's return. "I've got your tea ready. You must be worn out. How I hate having those doctors turning me inside out! I hope the news is good, Mrs. Callender?"

"No, it's not very good, thank you. The specialist says I must be operated on immediately."

"Well, I suppose if a specialist says you must, you must. Who knows, it might put you quite right again. You mustn't lose hope, my dear," exclaimed Mrs. Cornish. "I remember Mr. Cornish being taken with appendicitis and being rushed to the Cottage Hospital in Henley. I was in a state! But it was all right in the end. They're very clever these days."

"Is Christopher upstairs?" asked Mary, removing her hat.

"Sound asleep. He's been no trouble at all. Now don't you worry about that operation! Get it over and you'll have a new life. You can't go on suffering like this. It isn't human, my dear," observed Mrs. Cornish, bringing her a cup of tea from the table.

"I would have it without hesitation but for one thing. If anything went wrong, what would happen to Christopher? That's what haunts me," said Mary.

She turned round a vase of winter jasmine her son had gathered and put on the small table by her side, knowing how she loved flowers. Mrs. Cornish saw her hand tremble.

"The Lord'll look after Christopher—now don't you worry! Nothing will happen," said Mrs. Cornish.

"The Lord didn't look after Christopher when he was born," said Mary bitterly. "Why is he punished so? Why? Why? What will become of him!"

Mrs. Cornish made no reply. She felt there was no reply she could make. She looked at the clock and took her hat off the stand.

"I must be going. I told Mr. Cornish I'd be back at five. Do drink your tea, Mrs. Callender. I'll come in tomorrow evening for a few minutes. You want some more sugar, the canister's empty. Shall I bring a pound?"

"Please, and again, thank you very much, Mrs. Cornish."

IV

Forty-eight hours. It wasn't the pain that gnawed at her but the anxiety that kept her awake all night. Over and over she asked herself the question, what would become of her son if she died under the operation? There was no one to turn to. Her old aunt in Majorca was too feeble and too poor to offer Christopher a home. The question obsessed her all the next morning. Christopher, with the singular intuition that visited him at times, seemed to know she was troubled in her mind. He was attentive in odd little ways. He tried to help in the kitchen. He would not turn on his beloved radio because he feared she had a headache.

Soon after lunch Mary took her son out for a walk. Contrary to custom, she came home through the village and went to a telephone call-box. She rang up Dr. Woodfall and told him she would be ready to go into hospital on Friday, two days hence. He promised to make the necessary arrangements.

Mrs. Cornish, coming in to see her after tea, bringing a large cake she had made for Christopher, found her much easier in mind. When Mary told her that she had decided to go into hospital next Friday for the operation Mrs. Cornish asked what she would do about Christopher. She replied, "I've made the necessary arrangements. He'll be quite all right."

"I'm glad of that, Mrs. Callender. I talked it over last night with Mr. Cornish. He said he'd be glad for us to take in Christopher for a couple of weeks if it would help."

"That's very kind of you, you've been a wonderful

neighbour, Mrs. Cornish, but I shan't have to trouble you. I've arranged for Christopher to go away. I can never forget your kindness."

"Now don't you mention it! Mr. Cornish thinks you're the most wonderful woman in the world, and so do a lot of us. You can't imagine how Ethel Lovelock worries about not being allowed to come in to you, but Lovelock's a pigheaded fellow. I've a letter for you, the postman gave me it coming up."

Mary opened the letter. It was from Mrs. Anderson. They were leaving for six months in South Africa, to visit a married son.

Christopher came in at that moment, covered with dust. "Now what 'ave you been a-doing?" asked Mrs. Cornish genially. "You're all messed up!"

He tried to tell her.

"There are mice in the woodshed, he's always trying to catch them," said Mary.

Mrs. Cornish showed Christopher the cake. He flung his arms around her and hugged her, drooling in his delight.

On Thursday morning at a quarter to nine, Lovelock, waiting for the local bus into Henley, where he had a job, was astonished to see Mrs. Callender get into it also. He said good morning to her and went up to the upper deck. She made him feel uncomfortable. Ever since the episode with his wife at Juniper Cottage, any mention or sight of its occupants upset him. His wife would have gone back, but he put his foot down. "Mrs. Callender's no right 'arbouring that idiot son—he's a danger! He ought to be put in an asylum!" Ethel Lovelock disagreed. "The poor boy lost his head for once—after all, it's nature, isn't it? You were pretty randy at eighteen, I'll bet!" she exclaimed.

"I didn't go round tearing the clothes off girls!"

"That doesn't say you wouldn't like to! Look at the goings on of them soldiers over at Morton Barracks. A little bit of drink, and the lid's off with sex-starved lads. We're only human, I says."

"I draw the line at having my wife raped," retorted Lovelock. "He ought to be locked up!"

He saw Mrs. Callender get off the bus in Henley Market Place. Curious to know where she was going, he lingered by the Town Hall. He was astonished to see her walk up the hill and turn into the local police station on the corner of the street.

V

The police superintendent was writing at his desk when Mary Callender walked in.

"Good morning, madam," he said, coming to the counter between them.

"Good morning, officer. I am Mrs. Callender of Juniper Cottage near Easter Common. I have killed my son Christopher. I wish to give myself up."

She spoke very quietly. The superintendent stared at her. She certainly did not look mental. "But you never know these days" was his favourite expression.

"Now, madam, come, come! I hope you realise what you're saying? It's a pretty serious statement to make. Do you really mean it?"

"I mean every word. Tomorrow I am to enter hospital for a serious operation. I may not recover. I have a mentally deficient son and I won't leave him to the mercy of the world, so I've put Christopher to sleep. Last night I gave him a dose of aspirins and then placed a gas-tube in his mouth. My boy is quite dead."

Superintendent Wayne looked at the pale woman, slim, with greying hair and calm eyes, standing before him. Her speech was quite clear, she appeared wholly self-possessed though a little drawn. She looked a woman of about fifty, a lady obviously.

He called "Morgan!" A younger policeman came out of an adjoining room. The superintendent turned to the woman in front of him.

"You wish to make a statement? I must warn you, madam, that anything you say, and we put down, and you add your signature to, will be taken in evidence."

"I understand that, officer."

"Have you any near relation?"

"None at all."

"Who is your doctor?"

"Dr. Woodfall."

"Very well, I will take the statement. After reading it back to you, I will ask you to sign it."

He took a sheet of paper and after she had supplied him with full particulars of her name, age and residence, he carefully recorded the simple facts of her crime as she related it.

After the superintendent had slowly read over the statement she had made, she wrote her signature, in a firm, legible hand. She was then conducted to a small cell with a bunk and a chair. They brought her a rug and a glass of water. She heard the key turn in the lock.

CHAPTER VIII

I

THE Callender case created a great sensation not only in the district but all over the country. The story of a devoted mother who, fearing that she might not survive a serious operation, and leave her mental son uncared for, was carried in foreign as well as English newspapers. It also gained heavy headlines in the American and the colonial Press. There was nothing lacking to create a first-class drama of singular pathos. The papers resurrected the story of Hamilton Bostowell's conviction and suicide. There were photographs of Mary as a schoolgirl at Roedean, of her riding a camel in Egypt, of her Court presentation, and of her late husband, the handsome young naval officer lost in the Battle of Jutland.

The villagers at Easter Common lived in a sudden blaze of publicity. A bevy of pressmen and photographers descended upon the village seeking "human stories". Every detail was raked over. Everyone who had known or seen Mrs. Callender was subject to a merciless cross-examination. Ernest Lovelock, exasperated by the inquisition, smashed the camera of a photographer who waited in the ambush of a holly hedge for a close-up of his wife, Ethel. Every aspect of Juniper Cottage appeared in the illustrated papers.

The funeral of Christopher Callender, following the inquest, which normally would have been a quiet village affair, took on the semblance of a national event. The adjacent graves were trampled into a morass. A cordon of police vainly attempted to marshal the mob of automobilists who, in their ghoulish zest, came to desecrate the funeral of "the idiot boy" with their undisciplined curiosity. The fact that Christopher Callender was twenty-four at the time of his death was wholly ignored. He was the poor "idiot boy, helpless, and nursed by his devoted mother".

Mary Callender was brought before the Henley magistrates the Saturday following her surrender, a cold January day. Evidence was given by Superintendent Wayne and Dr. Woodfall, who had viewed the body in Juniper Cottage. At the coroner's inquest it was disclosed that death had not been due to the administration of aspirin, which had produced a soporific effect only, but to carbon-monoxide poisoning from gas administered through a rubber tube connected with a gas-ring. A detail that the Press made much of was that when the doctor and police superintendent found the body of Christopher Callender a posy of flowers was held between his hands.

After hearing the evidence in the police court, the Henley magistrates committed Mary Callender for trial at the Oxford Assizes. Immediately afterwards she was removed to Oxford Prison Hospital, where she underwent an operation. It was successful and she was retained in the hospital until the Assizes opened in March.

II

There was a short list, and the trial of Mrs. Mary Callender for the murder at Juniper Cottage of her son, Christopher, was the chief case at the Oxford Assizes. The court was crowded. A queue of spectators had stood outside the court-house since six o'clock in the morning. The case was heard by Mr. Justice Greverson, a little old man with gimlet eyes and a rat-trap mouth, famous for his taciturnity.

The counsel for the defence was Mr. Henry Summer. He was a young man of thirty-eight with a rapidly growing reputation at the Bar. The Callender case was one rung of the ladder by which he was destined to climb to one of the highest positions in the judiciary. He was an earnest, thin-faced man, with an aquiline nose and an eloquent mouth,

but of no special physical distinction except for two qualities
not immediately discernible. He had just come from a
sensational fraud case in which he had extricated his client,
one of five defendants, from what had appeared to be a hope-
less position. It was yet another of his successes with cases in
which a conviction seemed a foregone conclusion. Already
the court reporters, and the chief clerks in chambers, those
skilled spotters of forensic talent, were talking about "Summer
magic". They had seen the play of it so often, for Mr. Henry
Summer's two outstanding qualities, unveiled without os-
tentation, were an uncanny gift for beguiling the witness
into a mood of trustful confidence until the trap closed, and
a voice of such quiet-toned mellifluous beauty that it hypno-
tised both witnesses and jury. He had command of every
stop in an organ of great range. These two qualities were
allied with a sound legal knowledge and a shrewd assessment
of human nature.

The selection of Henry Summer was due to Mr. Charles
Simson, the Henley solicitor who had done the legal work
of the Callender family for forty years. His practice, conducted in an old Queen Anne house with a long garden
hidden from the High Street, was a family affair that had
gone from father to son through a hundred and fifty years.
Well known, highly respected, a benign man of sixty, he also
acted as the Magistrates' Clerk in the Henley court. In
addition he had been Mayor, a Steward of the Regatta
Committee, and, by virtue of having been one of the
Magdalen College eight that had rowed at the Regatta
forty years earlier, he had proudly worn, ever since, the pink
socks and tie of a member of the Leander Club. His real
fame, however, rested on being a wonderful rose grower, and
the father of a winner of the V.C. in the Great War.

It was to Mr. Charles Simson, following a telephone
enquiry from the Egyptian Embassy in London, that a cable,
signed Mohamed Kafi, had been forwarded. It ran: "Will
pay legal expenses of Callender defence. Engage finest

counsel." After a brief consultation with Colonel Anderson and Dr. Woodfall, the approach was made to Mr. Henry Summer.

The trial took place on the second day of the Oxford Assizes, at three o'clock on an early March afternoon. In accordance with custom, a plea of Not Guilty was entered to the charge of Wilful Murder.

Mary Callender was brought into court and given a seat in the dock. She was dressed in a simple grey costume. She was pale but self-possessed. When charged with the wilful murder of her son, Christopher Callender, she answered in a quiet voice, "Not Guilty".

Counsel for the Crown opened the case for the Prosecution. He stated the facts without emotion or emphasis. The accused was the mother of an imbecile son whom she had put to death, as the evidence would prove. It was a case of much pathos.

Her son, at the time of his death, twenty-four years of age, was entirely helpless and unable to speak. He had been a chronic invalid for many years, and an imbecile from birth. Mrs. Callender, a woman of very restricted means, fourteen years a widow, had been his constant nurse, watching over him day and night. For the last two years she had been in failing health and an essential operation had been postponed so long that her condition, due to a diseased kidney, had been aggravated to a point of real danger. The day before the alleged crime she had seen a specialist who informed her that an immediate operation was imperative. She had deferred her decision owing to her concern over the fate of her son, should the operation prove unsuccessful, and the difficulty of caring for him while she was in hospital. On the afternoon of the day of the alleged murder, Mrs. Callender had informed Dr. Woodfall that she would have the operation. That was on Wednesday afternoon. She agreed to enter the hospital the following Friday. At some time on the evening of Wednesday, it was alleged that Mrs. Callender had administered to her son a very heavy dose of aspirin, either to render him unconscious or bring about his death, and had made her intention doubly sure by placing in her son's mouth a rubber tube connected with the gas-supply. Death had resulted from carbon-monoxide poisoning. A witness, Mrs. Cornish, would be called to give evidence that she saw Christopher Callender alive on the afternoon of Wednesday, and spoke with him and his mother. She had brought them, from the grocer's store that she kept, a pound of sugar and a cake she had made for Christopher. She was the last person to visit the scene preceding the crime. No other person entered the cottage between her visit when she saw Christopher Callender alive on the Wednesday afternoon and the visit made by Superintendent Wayne of Henley, accompanied by Dr. Woodfall, on the following Thursday morning, as a result of the statement made earlier that same morning by Mrs. Callender to Superintendent Wayne at the police station.

The Prosecution then called the first witness, Dr. Woodfall, who described his finding of the body of Christopher Callender. Under cross-examination by Mr. Summer, he told the court that had not his patient, Mrs. Callender, undergone the operation, she would have been dead in six months, or earlier. He had informed her of this opinion, endorsed by the specialist, Mr. Dwight Mason, who examined her the day before the alleged murder. On the Wednesday afternoon, about three o'clock, Mrs. Callender had telephoned him to say that she would enter the hospital, on Friday, for the operation.

In cross-examination, Counsel for the Defence asked: "Would you say that, faced with the necessity of making a decision, Mrs. Callender's agony of mind was such that it upset her mental balance?"

"I most certainly think so," replied Dr. Woodfall.

The case for the prosecution lasted only an hour. Mr. Summer cross-examined the specialist, Mr. Dwight Mason.

In reply to a question, he said he told Mrs. Callender that if she did not have an immediate operation for the removal of an abscess on the kidney the result would be fatal. "She said to me, in considerable distress of mind, that she could not have the operation because she had a mental son and there was no one to take care of him while she was in hospital, or if the operation was unsuccessful." Within one week of his examination of Mrs. Callender he had performed the operation. His diagnosis had been correct. She could not possibly have lived many more weeks. She had now made a complete recovery.

Mr. Summer's speech on behalf of the accused was short, and simple in statement. It was, he said, a case of extreme poignancy which the jury in all human probability would never experience again. It was the story of a woman who, after a harrowing tragedy in her youth, had experienced a brief happiness before being subject to the loss of a beloved husband, a gallant officer who had died for his country. From her widowhood on she was faced with the grim necessity, alone and in circumstances that were not easy, of nursing through infancy, childhood, adolescence and early manhood a terribly afflicted son.

"Gentlemen of the jury, here are none of the passions usually to be found in the crime of murder. Instead of brutality and malice we find unselfish love and patient devotion, which make a strange paradox in this case, for here there is no mean or callous motive, no desire to be rid of a helpless son. For twenty-four years, day and night, a mother's care has been unceasing. Suffering herself from great bodily weakness, in considerable pain and increasing exhaustion, she was ever the same devoted mother. Every witness in this case has told the same poignant story, that in each change of circumstance her thoughts were only for her boy. Without any help, any relaxation, any respite, she has struggled on. Never has there been a case of a more sublime example of a mother's devotion. I do not know what verdict

you will feel impelled to give, having heard the facts produced by the Prosecution, but whatever it may be, I do not
see how it can be insensible to or divorced from the great
quality of mercy. For in this court today the immeasurable
depth of a mother's love is being weighed in our hearts
against the solemn act of one who sought, at great cost to
herself, to save her child from suffering and neglect." Counsel
concluded with a quotation:

> *Not the King's crown nor the deputed sword,*
> *The Marshal's truncheon nor the Judge's robe,*
> *Becomes them with one half so good a grace*
> *As mercy does.*

There was a deep silence when Counsel finished, broken
only by someone sobbing at the back of the court.

The light was fading in the early spring afternoon when
the judge began his summing up. It weighed heavily against
the accused, but at the end there was an indication to the
jury. He alluded to the moving speech of Counsel for the
Defence. "It may be described fairly as an appeal to you to
add a recommendation to the verdict that you will probably
feel it is your duty to return."

The jury was absent only a few minutes. They returned
with a verdict of "Guilty". The foreman of the jury added
to his reply: "We wish to make the strongest possible recommendation to mercy." There was a burst of applause from
the crowded court, sternly checked. Before the judge
assumed the black cap for passing sentence, the clerk of
assize asked the prisoner if she had anything to say why the
sentence of the court should not be passed on her.

Mary Callender stood perfectly still between the two
female warders, a small thin figure in grey, her fine face
framed in its straight silvering hair. Then, after a heavy
silence, her voice, in a natural tone, said quietly: "I did it
in mercy."

The judge put on the black cap and without any preamble passed on the prisoner the sentence of death.

III

Three days after the death sentence the Press carried headings: "Condemned mother receives pardon." On the Home Secretary's recommendation, following the jury's rider, the King had granted a reprieve of the death sentence and a pardon to Mrs. Mary Callender.

Her solicitor, Mr. Simson, brought the news to her cell. "In a little while, I do not doubt, you will be free. You'll have a warm welcome back to Juniper Cottage."

"I don't think I could ever live there again," said Mary Callender. "I suppose the best thing would be for me to go abroad. I have an old aunt living in Majorca. She wrote just before my trial that if all went well I was to go out to her."

"I'm afraid that isn't possible any longer, Mrs. Callender," said Mr. Simson quietly. "I'm sorry to inform you that Mrs. Cavan died a week before the trial. We thought it wise to withhold the news from you owing to the strain you were undergoing."

"Poor Aunt Helen! I fear the shock killed her. It's the second time she'd faced a trial. She was wonderful all the time of my father's tragedy. She was a kind, brave soul," said Mary Callender, her voice trembling.

"Since she attained a good age, eighty-one, perhaps it wasn't from shock," observed Mr. Simson. "I have a letter from her solicitors informing me that you will inherit, together with the Villa Hoya at Sóller, a sum of about two thousand pounds after death duty has been paid on the estate. We are hoping your release won't be long delayed. There have been questions asked in the House of Commons, and from the tone of the Home Secretary's reply I think it will come pretty soon. The pressure of public opinion has been very strong. Are you well treated here? I understand there's no intention of moving you."

"I have nothing at all to complain of, Mr. Simson. Indeed, I am deeply grateful to everyone for the kindness shown to me," said Mary Callender.

"Then you've no request to make?"

"None, thank you."

IV

Two weeks passed, then one morning she was taken before the Governor.

"I am pleased to inform you, Mrs. Callender, that you are to be released tomorrow morning at eight o'clock. Your solicitor has been informed and will make the necessary arrangements. May I congratulate you, and express the hope that you will find peace and happiness for the rest of your life," he said.

She left the room a little dazed. It was strange, but now that release from prison was imminent she was a little afraid of the world outside.

She slept badly that night, and ate no breakfast. It was a sharp, clear March morning when the warder conducted her to a small room. Here she found Mr. Simson, Dr. Woodfall, and, to her surprise and pleasure, Mrs. Cornish with a bunch of flowers. She came forward and embraced Mary Callender who, for the first time during her ordeal, burst into tears.

The secret of the release had been well kept. There was no one at the prison gates, where the doctor's car awaited them. Mary was to stay for a few days with the Simsons until she had completed her plans for the future.

CHAPTER IX

I

THE words of the lesson read by the Reverend Tobias Smollett had their own particular appropriateness for Mary Callender, coming as they did on the twenty-fifth day of March, 1951. It was the twentieth anniversary of her release from Oxford Prison, an anniversary of which the Reverend Tobias Smollett could have no possible knowledge.

Many waters cannot quench love, neither can the floods drown it. Twenty years was a long time and Mary Callender sometimes wondered if she could be the same woman as the one who had stood trial for murder, been sentenced to death, and reprieved. So many were dead who belonged to that dark background: Mr. Simson, Dr. Woodfall, Mrs. Cornish, Mohamed Kafi, the kind Andersons. She sold her aunt's little house in Sóller, and Juniper Cottage. After the sale of the Villa Hoya she spent six months with the widowed Mrs. Harcourt, still living in Seville. But the need of a place of her own and the longing for England brought her home. Out of a visit paid to Philip Harcourt at Malaga, married, with two small children, came something that brought her pleasure and profit. She wrote down the bedtime stories with which she had amused Philip's children, and they were published in London. The book had a modest success and she wrote three more books before she felt she had exhausted her vein.

Her pension, with the addition of her aunt's legacy and her earnings as an author, was adequate to her modest needs. On returning to London she took a little apartment in Regent's Park and lived there until it was bombed in the Second World War. She remained in London throughout the war, having found interesting work as a receptionist at a

Red Cross Blood Bank. One day a young officer came to
donate his blood. His name evoked a memory and she could
not resist asking him a question.

"Greverson? That's an unusual name. Are you related to
Mr. Justice Greverson?"

"Yes, I'm his grandson. Did you know him?"

"Very slightly," she replied.

"I loved the old boy. Very good to me as a kid, and left
me everything," said young Greverson.

"Oh, he's dead?"

"Yes, quite sad, his end. He blew his brains out in his flat
in Queen Anne's Mansions. Chronic melancholia. He'd lost
his wife. Poor old boy!"

II

When the war ended her doctor sent her to Abano, near
Venice, to take a cure for rheumatism. From there she went
for a brief stay in San Remo. One day she made an excursion
to Ligurio and was delighted with the little town curving
around its bay of golden sand. She heard of a small villa to
let, furnished, set in an old olive-grove behind the English
church. She lived in it for a year, then bought it very
cheaply. With some of the furniture in the villa she took on
old Laura, stone-deaf. Her affliction was a protection against
gossip.

The Villa Chiara also was incommunicable. In it Mrs.
Callender, as throughout so much of her life, was a recluse.
She seldom went out, she seldom received. No one in Ligurio
knew the tragedy of her life. They found her a quiet-man-
nered, pleasant-looking elderly woman. They did not know
even that she had written children's books. She told no one
of the fact. The only two villas to which she went were Sir
Aubrey Wellington's and Lady Crossley's. Their owners
were both interesting persons, musical, well read and with
minds above gossip and the endless bridge that consumed the
lives of most of the English colony.

One o'clock struck in the Municipio as she lay on the chaise-longue in the Villa Chiara. Its clock never agreed with St. Ambrogio's. The parish church's clock was always behind the Municipio's, or, as the *parroco* preferred to put it, the Municipio's clock was always in front of St. Ambrogio's.

"We have no clock. If we had, we'd have to come in half-way between the sacred and the profane," said the Reverend Tobias Smollett, delighted with his little joke.

Laura the maid ignored the municipal clock and followed St. Ambrogio.

Mary Callender got up from the chaise-longue. The telephone was ringing down in the hall. Laura never heard it, just as she never heard the visitors' bell. Happily, neither rang frequently.

"*Pronto!*" said Mary, having reached the receiver.

"Oh, Mrs. Callender! Meriel Crossley speaking. I missed you coming out of church. John has an old friend and his wife coming tomorrow for a few days. We're giving a small luncheon party for them on Tuesday, at one o'clock. About a dozen. We hope you'll come. It's two new faces in Ligurio!" said Lady Crossley with a laugh.

"Thank you. I'd love to," replied Mary.

"Splendid! Wasn't old Tobias funny this morning with his *Song of Solomon*? We haven't many roes running about on our mountains! Mrs. Gavin thought it disgusting and wouldn't stay to Communion. I thought it funny. After all, it is in the Bible, and isn't quite *Lady Chatterley's Lover!* Tuesday, then. Good-bye!"

She rang off. Laura announced lunch.

III

She arrived a few minutes before one at the Crossleys'. Most of the guests had already arrived and were drinking cocktails on the long covered terrace with its magnificent view of the Mediterranean between the twin headlands of the bay. There were the usual agreeable faces, the Smolletts, Sir Aubrey Wellington, lively Mrs. Viviani in a powder-blue dress and a black Córdoba felt hat that gave her a Carmen air, Commander Maysmith, Ligurio's prize exhibit, a nonagenarian dandy advertising Savile Row, his wife, chic Maude Maysmith, the Count and Countess Verdecampo di Saluzzo, Mrs. Dove, with a hat that was no hat at all, being an aureole of silver leaves, as befitted her name and nature, and the Crossleys' house guests, Lord and Lady Brookman.

Sir John greeted Mary warmly. He liked her and regretted that she came so seldom. He introduced her to the Brookmans. Lord Brookman was a tallish, fresh-complexioned man with hair greying over the temples. He had a distinguished bearing. They had hardly exchanged a word before the Countess Verdecampo seized him. They had met two years before in Delhi where he had headed a British Delegation. Mary turned to Lady Brookman and learned they were departing on the morrow after two weeks in Italy. They had been attending a conference in Rome dealing with the slave traffic. Mary suppressed a smile. So they were still dealing with the slave traffic! Mohamed Kafi had not been wrong.

Presently they went in to lunch. As always the food was excellent. The Crossley arrangement of silver and flowers never looked better on the shining mahogany table. Mary was seated between Count Verdecampo and Maysmith. She was talking with the count when a voice came down the table. It was Lord Brookman's. He was telling a story about Roosevelt and Churchill when he had accompanied a war mission to Washington. The table quietened and listened deferentially. It was a voice of singular attraction and he told his story well.

Suddenly Mary Callender's heart gave a quick beat. Something in the intonation struck a chord of memory. The voice, the manner, she could not be mistaken—they were, incontestably, those of the man who had conducted her defence twenty years ago. The Lord Brookman speaking on

Lady Crossley's right, holding the table engrossed, was Henry Summer, her counsel at the Oxford Assizes twenty years ago. Older, heavier, lined, with greying hair, she could now discover in him the brilliant young lawyer of that time. The aquiline nose, the eloquent wide mouth, were the same. But the face, she saw, was now stamped with a deeper authority.

At the conclusion of the story the guests laughed appreciatively. The conversation became general. Mary found herself answering Count Verdecampo without knowing what he had been saying. For the first time in her life she experienced a surge of panic which she had to fight to suppress. The rest of the luncheon had an unreality. If they only knew the drama of her situation! But they did not. Lord Brookman himself was unaware of her identity. The white hair of a woman of seventy had come to her aid.

The lunch ended, they moved into the large drawing-room with its English furniture. While the men lingered over their coffee in the dining-room, Mary, now in control of herself, sought out her hostess.

"Tell me, your attractive Lord Brookman—who is he? Have you known him very long?" asked Mary.

"Henry? Yes. He was Sir Henry Summer, the famous K.C., before he was made Lord Brookman. John met him in Uganda. He came out on some Government mission in the last year that John was stationed there. It was just before he retired. He wasn't Lord Brookman then. Isn't he charming? And I like Julie his wife—such a sense of humour!" said Lady Crossley.

The men came in. Mary talked a while, but she wanted to get away. The Smolletts were the first to leave. She rose to follow them. The moment came when she said good-bye to Lord and Lady Brookman.

"Do you live here, Mrs.——" He hesitated, seeking the name.

"Callender—Mary Callender," she said.

"Forgive me—my wife always scolds me for being so bad with names when introduced."

She knew the lapse was deliberate. Their eyes had met in recognition of each other.

"Yes, I have lived here almost five years, very quietly," she said, taking up his question.

"How fortunate you are!" he said, smiling.

"I was not always so fortunate," she replied.

He held her hand warmly, retaining it for a few moments.

"If I lived here, under this blue sky, I feel I should forget everything that had ever worried me," he said, gaiety in his voice and smile.

"Good-bye, Lord Brookman!"

"Good-bye, Mrs. Callender."

She passed out into the hall. The Smolletts, seeing her, said: "We can give you a lift."

"Thank you, but I'll walk, it's such a short way."

"Ah, perhaps you don't feel safe with the Church!" cried the Reverend Tobias waggishly, as he proceeded to enter their car.

Mary Callender was surprised at her answer.

"Just now I feel safe anywhere," she said, and waved good-bye.

CHAPTER I

I

THE houses in Library Avenue looked all alike. A similar pattern could be found in all the small towns across the United States, from Maine to Florida, from New Jersey to California; and here, before the long transcontinental railroad ended its long ascent over the Great Divide, the pattern was kept in Laramie, Wyoming.

Miss Allerton loved Library Avenue. She liked its graceful sycamore trees that made a green cathedral-nave in summer of the wide road with its grassed sidewalks. She liked all the houses with their open verandas and classical porticoes. Occasionally there was a deviation from the pattern. Some of the columns were Ionic, most of them were Doric. One of the porticoes, an elegant rebel, had Corinthian columns, magnificent fluted shafts with capitals of acanthus leaves. There was a subtle reason for this deviation, which Miss Allerton always delighted in explaining to her guests. "You see that porch with the Corinthian columns? It's an architectural pun!"

"An architectural pun? What do you mean?" queried the puzzled guest, whose reaction on hearing this statement never varied.

"We had a banker who retired many years ago and built himself that house. His name was David Corinth, so he felt he must have Corinthian columns!"

Miss Allerton was always delighted with the smile her explanation produced, and followed it up with her next statement, a test of intelligence. ("Only a few get it," she would say.) "The Blochs who live opposite said that that was no reason for them to change their porch, which has Doric columns!"

She would look at her guest's blank face. "No, she didn't get it, not very bright, my dear," she would comment, relating the incident later. "Not columns, but blocks!" she would explain. Then Miss Allerton gave a soft little laugh. She knew that many people thought her crazy, and rather enjoyed the rôle.

In the fading afternoon she walked up the path between the open lawns, and for a moment regretted that she would not see the spring, nor sit in the rocking-chair on the veranda during the summer heat. Today a sharp wind reddened her cheeks. In March, Laramie, at a height of seven thousand feet, could be arctic.

There were letters in the metal receptacle at the side of the door. One of them, with its inscription on the long envelope, made her heart give a jump. *Olympia Tours*, ran the title. The tickets had come!

Her hand was a little shaky as she put the key in the lock, and for the first time in many years Socrates, approaching her over the hall carpet, lacked a greeting. His tail stiff in the air, he brushed against her fur coat and drew no endearing comment. Miss Allerton walked straight through into the sitting-room, picked up a paper-knife and opened the long envelope. The contents fell out over the desk. There they were—the tickets to a new world, the world she had dreamed of for thirty years.

She sat down and opened one folder after another. A ticket with drawing-room-sleeper to Chicago, a ticket with the Chicago–New York flight, in a yellow cover. A ticket with the New York–Rome flight, in a green cover.

She pressed the green cover between her hands and closed her eyes. She saw the dome of St. Peter's, Michelangelo's dome; and the Pope in his palace, a little to the right, standing in a window from which he blessed the crowd in the piazza below. She knew the piazza with the two fountains and the Bernini columns, from a film she had seen in a Laramie cinema recently. She saw the Forum with the columned Arch of Septimius Severus at the lower end, the Arch of Titus at the top end. She saw the Colosseum, she saw the tombs and pine trees on the Via Appia, the brown Tiber flowing by the broken bridge, known to Macaulay's noble Romans: "Lo! I will stand on thy right hand and keep the bridge with thee!" She saw the Temple of Vesta, with its shallow brown-tiled roof like a saucy girl's summer straw hat. She saw the great golden drum of the Castle of St. Angelo, with the bronze angel on the summit, flashing a sword in the air that arrested the plague; and the rampart from which La Tosca had jumped in the opera. She had heard Puccini's opera on the radio last night and it had had a new meaning for her ears.

She sat quite still, holding the flight ticket in her hands. Socrates jumped up into her lap. She put her arms around him, hugging him. "Socrates!" she cried, "I'm going to Rome, to Rome, Socrates!"

The cat struggled a little impatiently. Rome meant nothing to him. The saucer was empty on the kitchen floor.

From her chair by the window she overlooked the broad wooden veranda and the lawn. The trees of Library Avenue raised an iron filigree against the sky with their black leafless branches. She was all alone in the house. Mary, the daily woman who came in, had left. Her nephew, Homer, was at a baseball game. Loneliness had never troubled her in this old house where she had been born and where she had nursed her mother until her death. For some years there had been young life in the house when her sister's orphaned children had been taken in, following their parents' death in a dreadful train accident. She had watched over them for fourteen years, but now they had fled the fold.

She was left alone. That was always the fate of the faithful spinster daughter who remained to look after Mother. When Mother had gone, who remained to look after the devoted daughter? No one. Her two younger sisters had seen the warning light early. One had married at twenty, the other at twenty-two. When her father had died it was not possible to leave an invalid mother alone. So they had settled down in this house in Library Avenue where she had been born. She loved the home in which she had lived for fifty-three years. She had loved her mother whom she had nursed and supported for fifteen years, for the Allerton fortune had not been sufficient to sustain the ever-rising cost of living, and suddenly, after the appalling Nevada train accident, two small children, a boy of seven and a girl of ten, were on her hands. They had been a rewarding liability and all of Grace Allerton's loving nature had flowered in the care of these orphans.

To ensure their adequate education she had gone back to her work as art mistress at Laramie High School. The trip to Italy, mother of all art, planned and saved for in 1939, was postponed. A world war and the rise in the cost of living had cancelled all hope of the great tour of Europe. By way of consolation Miss Allerton took Italian lessons from an Italian refugee family that had opened a fruit-shop in Laramie. She loved the noisy Brandini family (with a lustrous-eyed baby to mark every year of the calendar) from whom she took lessons in exchange for English ones. She had progressed considerably in two years when, by accident, encountering an Italian film actress on a train, she learned, to her dismay, that she was fluent in a Neapolitan gutter dialect. Undaunted, she began all over again with her vowels, aided by a gramophone disc. As an extra corrective she had laboriously followed a radio course on Dante.

In the next few years her mother died and the war dragged on. When the war ended the Italian trip was still an unrealised dream. Her niece and nephew had left home for college. She was utterly alone. And now it was 1953, her sabbatical year at the school. She could have twelve months' holiday with pay. After the Hebrew pattern, on this seventh year, she would be released from slavery. No, not slavery.

She loved her work and her pupils, but the cage had been closed so long about her that she felt her wings would soon be too feeble for flight. Habit encroached on the spirit of adventure. As age approached one wanted to know instinctively just where were the matches by the kitchen stove, to find the same indentation in the nightly mattress, the same reading-lamp within reach, and all the comfortable old shoes in line in the bottom of the wardrobe.

In the year 1953 Miss Allerton knew it was now or never. She was not good at now-or-never. There had been a now-or-never crisis in 1932. A young automobile agent, who had sold the Allertons a new automobile, had continued to call long after the transaction had been completed. After two months' attention he had proposed a clandestine week-end, which she had indignantly rejected. At the end of five rather turbulent months he had proposed marriage. It came in the form of an ultimatum. He had bought an agency in Des Moines which included a house over the showroom. She knew that, at the age of thirty-two, it was the last ring of the bell. There was the problem of her mother. "We'll stow the old dame away somewhere," he said brusquely. The remark underlined the coarse streak in him. He was hot-handed, a handsome, thick-set sexy young man of twenty-eight. He had an ebullient warmth about him, he made money easily and spent it generously. He bought the "old dame" expensive boxes of candy, almost man-handled her when he kissed her, called her "Mom", and took her by storm. But Grace discovered that he drank heavily and was paying maintenance for a seven-year-old child in Creston. He had an infectious good nature and was a born gambler with life. There was no doubt that he was in love with her, but he was in love with her as an object of sex and not as Grace Allerton. Yet it was for none of these reasons, after a month of agonising debate, that she rejected him. He had big red hands and breathed hard whenever he touched her. More offensive was his crudeness, the awful badges he sported on his jacket. He delighted in them, the larger the better—Rotary, Kiwanis, Lions, Elks, Buffaloes, and an endless succession of gaudy, beribboned rosettes from the various trade conferences he attended up and down the State.

When she said "No" he took it with a sportive good humour. "You'll live to regret it, my girl. You'd have had kids and happiness. Now all you'll have is old Mom and an empty bed."

He killed himself four months later on an ice-bound road crossing the Rockies. To her amazement he had willed her all he had, a share in his agency, a fishing shack, clothes and fifteen hundred dollars in the bank. In all, she inherited nearly four thousand dollars. Full of remorse, his drawbacks dissolved in the warmth of her memory of him, she kept his photograph, black-haired, smiling, on her dressing-table. The legacy sent her niece and nephew through college. "He must have been a good guy," said young Homer, looking at Auntie's bull-necked swain with the halo of a sporting end. "He was," replied his aunt, with an undertone of emotion. Such was her first now-or-never. She liked to think that she had lived to regret it, but was not too sure.

The second now-or-never had presented itself with that legacy of four thousand dollars. Here was the chance to travel at last; but her mother fell ill, the trip to Italy was postponed. There followed the tragedy of the train wreck, with two orphans to be cared for. Would there be enough to send Homer and Anne through the university after a trip to Italy? She carefully examined the figures and realised that by subtracting two thousand dollars from four she would be jeopardising their futures. That she would never do. Rome, Florence and Venice were not to be for some time, perhaps never, most certainly not now.

The years marched on. Her mother died, the children grew up. In 1940 she had to put a new roof on 17 Library Avenue. After 1940 the cost of living began to rise. By 1947, just when her niece and nephew were due for college, it rose alarmingly. The legacy melted away and with it some of her savings. It seemed clear that the Italian tour had passed from the "now" to the "never" category.

But Miss Allerton had an irrepressible faith in the goodness of life. She looked at Homer and Anne. What rewarding, affectionate untroublesome charges they had been! She would not let herself dwell on her loneliness now they had left the fold. God in His mercy had spared Homer from a frightful war, having been born late enough. He was back from Japan, his military service finished, and, a Stanford graduate, had a splendid opportunity with an engineering firm in San Francisco. And Anne, now a Doctor of Music, she need not be anxious about her.

She was a little worried to find no letter in her box from Anne, who had been more than a year at her post in the University of Beirut. Her appointment as an assistant professor of music had caught out Miss Allerton in her geography, which she had always believed to be good. When she had greeted Anne on her way through from Berkeley, California, to New York, on the first lap of her journey to Europe, she had expressed her joy over the appointment.

"Wonderful! To think you'll be at the very heart of the great Wagner Festival. How useful your German will be!" she exclaimed, as she motored her niece home from Laramie station.

"But, Auntie darling, I'm going to Beirut, where they don't speak German!"

"Surely, darling, in Germany they speak German?"

"Auntie, you're confusing Beirut with Bayreuth. I'm going to Lebanon in Syria, not to Germany."

In her astonishment Miss Allerton ran right though a red traffic light, without mishap. It was exciting to go anywhere outside of Laramie. To go to Europe was wonderful, but to go to Asia Minor was fabulous.

The moment they were home she got out the atlas. They turned up the map of Lebanon and Syria.

"There," said Anne, putting her finger where the new state of Lebanon bordered the Mediterranean sea.

"At the foot of Mount Lebanon. Oh, Anne, you'll see the cedars that Solomon built his Temple with!" exclaimed Miss Allerton breathlessly.

"They tell me there are very few cedars left," said Anne.

Her aunt's finger travelled over the map. "Beirut, Homs, Damascus, Tyre, Sidon," she murmured, her voice enchanted. "Anne, it's a poem of travel!" She closed her eyes and recited:

I am the gate toward the sea; O sailor men, pass out from me.
I hear you high on Lebanon, singing the marvels of the sea.

"James Elroy Flecker wrote that. How do you get there?"

"Plane to Rome, then via Athens," said Anne.

"Rome! You're going to Rome?"

Anne knew her aunt's obsession. She felt a little unkind with her good fortune. She put her arms around her and kissed her.

"Darling Auntie, one day you'll get to Rome, even if I have to come and fetch you!" she said.

"Of course I shall!" answered Miss Allerton stoutly, challenging an impossibility.

And now in the April of the year of grace 1953, her sabbatical year, she was going to Rome. The miracle had been achieved. Young Albert Brandini, the eldest of the seven Brandini boys, had worked the miracle. He was employed in a local realty office. One day he had called on her with a proposal.

"You know, Miss Allerton, your back garden's too big," he said, as soon as he had sat down.

"Yes, I often wish it was smaller, Albert. Jobbing gardeners are so dear these days," she replied, agreeing.

"If you had less garden there would be less expense."

"That's true, Albert. But what can I do? It's there, and

it must be kept in order, and Homer's no longer here to help."

"You know Mr. Butler, who lives beyond the bottom of your garden—a big fat man with those skinny boys?"

"Yes, but our relations are not very cordial," said Miss Allerton with a smile. "His retriever will chase poor Socrates, set on by those boys. I've twice written a note of protest."

"Mr. Butler ain't a bad guy, really. Well, Miss Allerton, he'd like a piece of your garden, and he won't be mean about it."

"What does he want it for?" asked Miss Allerton suspiciously.

"His kids are growing and they want a tennis-court. I think he's a bit scared of you and afraid you might stick your neck out if he approached you. I told him I knew you'd be reasonable if he'd let me handle it."

Albert Brandini smiled over the cup of coffee she had given him. He knew that she had a liking for him, which was true. As a boy he had seemed very graceful in Miss Allerton's eyes, with his black curls, melting dark eyes and beautiful brown legs. He was a born Romeo.

She looked at him for a moment, and then said, "But, Albert, I don't know that I want to sell any of the garden."

"Aw, Miss Allerton, you've said the garden's too large and worries you. It isn't as if he wanted to put up a shanty. It's only a tennis-court he wants. It wouldn't be an obstruction."

"I'll have to think about it, Albert. How much would he give—how much of the garden does he want?"

"Thirty yards, about up to your fountain. He'd grow a hedge across, of course. And he'd give you fifteen hundred dollars, and pay expenses," said Albert. "That's a good price. I jacked him up from a thousand."

"You've been discussing it?"

"Well, on and off. I told him I'd sound you. Of course you don't have to sell, but the garden does worry you, doesn't it?"

"Yes, Albert, it does. Well, thank you, I'll think about it."

"Very well, Miss Allerton," said Albert, rising. He thanked her for the coffee. He always had beautiful manners. There had been a time when she thought of him as a choice for Anne, but nothing came of it.

"I'll be getting along," he said, and then, hat in hand, he paused in the doorway and said gently, his soft dark eyes smiling, "Fifteen hundred dollars is a good sum of money, Miss Allerton."

"It certainly is—when you haven't got it," agreed Miss Allerton with a smile.

"Yes, quite a lot," mused Albert, lingering on the veranda and stooping to stroke Socrates. "You could have quite a holiday in Italy with that."

Miss Allerton looked at him keenly. "And how do you know I want to have a holiday in Italy?" she asked.

He pushed back his black curls with a thin brown Latin hand before putting on his hat. "You've always said you'd like to go to Italy, ever since I was a kid—and wasn't that why you took lessons from Emilia? I'd go like a shot with a thousand bucks in my pocket!"

"I must think about it very seriously," said Miss Allerton, her heart pounding from the arrow that had gone home.

"Sure, there ain't no hurry. Good-bye, Miss Allerton."

Her gave her the graceful bow and smile that sprang from his ancestral blood, and went down the path. Miss Allerton watched the sprightly young Romeo affectionately, and slowly closed her door.

Albert Brandini felt confirmed in the belief that he was a born realty salesman. She would sell, he had no doubt. He had touched her weakness. He liked Miss Allerton a lot; he liked her still more because he felt he had made for himself a neat sum of two hundred dollars. Mr. Butler, anxious, had offered him that if he pulled off the deal.

Miss Allerton thought over the offer all night. She woke a little before six in the morning with it on her mind, and turned on the bedside lamp. A volume of Hare's *Walks in Rome* lay on the bedside table. Last night she had read a chapter in it about the Forum, possibly for the third time. Restless, she got up, put on a dressing-gown and went downstairs to make a pot of tea. Socrates was astonished by this early appearance and sat up on his cushion.

"It's no use, Socrates, I just can't sleep. That Brandini boy's wrecked my night!"

As she put on the kettle the old grandfather clock struck the hour. *Rome! Rome! Rome! Rome! Rome! Rome!* it declared in her ears. Certainly she was obsessed, the clock could not have said anything of the kind. It was wholly English and had *Manson, London* written on its brass dial. It had stood for fifty years in her grandfather's house at Nantucket. He related that his father, captain of a whaler, had brought it from Bristol after a trip to England on a clipper.

While the kettle boiled she peered into the garden. It was damp and misty in the dim light, but she could see the piece of land beyond the fountain that Mr. Butler coveted, and the ugly water-tank on its tripod beyond the trees. She tried to imagine the hedge that Albert said he would plant. Certainly she would never miss that plot. It was difficult to believe that she could exchange that damp, misty piece of a lawn for Rome shining under a bright blue sky, with the dome of St. Peter's in the distance instead of that ugly aluminium water-tank.

The kettle boiled. She made the tea, took a biscuit out of a tin and sat down. The kitchen was very tidy. Mary, the daily woman, kept it spotless. Socrates leapt on to her lap. She stroked his head.

"Yes, I'm going to do it," she said decisively, "and you can stay with Mary till I'm back."

II

And she had done it. Here she was, this March afternoon, with the tickets. On Tuesday she left for Italy. Even now she could not quite believe it, and in doing it she had gone right over the dam and drowned a principle that had been sacred to the Allertons for generations. They had all looked on hire-purchase as the lure of the devil. If they could not pay cash down for a thing they went without it. She remembered a crisis in the family when she was a small girl. Mabel, her younger sister, wanted to learn the piano. They had not got a piano. There were pianos for sale on the hire-purchase plan in a shop on Main Street. Mrs. Allerton suggested, furtively, getting Mabel a piano in this way. A chasm opened in the Allerton household. Mr. Allerton stormed and drew a horrifying portrait of bankruptcy in the home, and profligate children ending in gaol for debt. In the end Mabel got her piano, but it was bought cash down. The Allerton family sacrificed their summer holiday to enable Mary to learn Czerny's *One Hundred and One Exercises*. The folly of it was that she gave up practising after a year's lessons and the piano lid was seldom raised.

Miss Allerton now recalled that dead crisis evoked by the instalment plan. Here she was, the first to break the family principle. Obviously it was foolish to travel all that way to Italy and only stay for a few weeks. She was a free woman for a whole year. Rome, Assisi, Siena, Florence, Milan and Venice were all within a few hours' journey from each other. There was enough to see in the art galleries of these places to keep her occupied for a year. But fifteen hundred dollars would only procure a couple of months abroad, with care. She had been dismayed by the cost of the tickets. It was during her preoccupation with costs that she had picked up a travel magazine, bought for its colour photographs of Italy. In it she saw an advertisement of one of the airlines, offering return flights to Europe, the fare payable with a small sum down and the rest in a year's monthly instalments. Reluctant to overthrow the family's principle, enticed, perturbed, she took paper and pencil and figured it out. By paying the fare from her monthly stipend she would have enough left, adding some savings, for a year abroad. She figured it out four times to make sure she had not lost her wits. When the next day she diffidently mentioned the instalment plan for paying her fare to the young man in the *Olympia Tours* bureau, he showed not the slightest hesitation.

"Do you think it's quite all right? I've never done this sort of thing before," she asked.

"Sure it's all right! Everybody's doing it, Miss Allerton."

"But supposing I died before I'd paid all the——"

"Now, Miss Allerton, you ain't going to die! We all know you. You're one of the nippiest women in Laramie. You taught my sister. I've heard her talk of you. She thinks you're a mighty fine woman."

"Oh, thank you."

"And suppose you did die, suppose the plane crashed, which it won't, aren't you insured?"

"Why, yes, I am," answered Miss Allerton.

"Well, there you are, we'd just collect. Now fill in this form and sign it. I'll fix the rest."

The rest had been fixed. She had the tickets, and with some of her savings added, two thousand dollars in travellers' cheques. And all she had lost was a little piece of bothersome lawn. In exchange, almost a year in Italy was hers.

She would have to live carefully in Italy. It was a good thing for some Americans to live cheaply in Europe. The people over there had a preposterous idea that every American was a millionaire, with an enormous Cadillac car and a gigantic frigidaire from which endless parties were fed. These ostentatious new automobiles, two yards out in front, and two yards out behind, she considered to blame also, and quite vulgar. "I suppose we have to have such long bodies because we have such short pedigrees," she commented when somebody was awestruck by the Keinblochs' new automobile. The Keinblochs were a loud, brash family that always played the radio fortissimo through open windows with all the lights on, and owed money all round.

She had been fortunate in planning her Italian trip. Miss Allport, who had made the grand tour and was very knowledgeable on how to keep costs down to eight dollars a day— "You take half-pension and have a snack lunch wherever you are"—had given her addresses in Rome and Florence. In Rome the Pensione Gigli had a balcony with a view over the gardens of the Villa Medici, as far as St. Peter's on the horizon. In Florence the Pensione Rigatti was on the fourth floor of an old palace on the Lungarno. It had an open loggia from which you saw the Ponte Vecchio, the dome on the Duomo and Giotto's tower. "Don't forget if you have a boiled egg for breakfast, it's extra. Egg in Italian is *uovo*. I asked the maid for a boiled *uva* and she was puzzled to death. Finally she brought the landlady, Signora de Benedicitis, such a lovely name for a lovely woman, and it seems I'd asked for a boiled grape! I'd said *uva bollito* for *uovo bollito*. And another thing, my dear, don't let the hotels put stamps on your letters. They go on the bill and you pay fifteen per cent. for service on the total. But they're such nice, kind people otherwise," concluded Miss Allport.

She had made careful notes of all this. She had studied the Baedeker maps of Rome and Florence. She would not have to take taxis, she could go in buses. Her Italian was sufficient to ask the way. "*Per favore, signora, dove prendo il bus per San Pietro?*" No, it was not at all difficult really.

A week ago another idea had come into her head. Would it be possible for Anne, at the Easter holiday, to come to Rome from Beirut? On the map it did not look such a long way. It was nothing like the distances they travelled in America. That was the wonderful thing about Europe. You could see London, Paris, Lucerne, Florence, Rome, Venice, Vienna and Athens, and even then you hadn't gone as far as from Laramie to New York. So she had written to Anne informing her of her advent in Rome for Easter, and asking if there was any possibility of her coming there to join her. She had hoped there would be an air-mail letter in reply any

day now. That was why she was disappointed there had been
no letter in the mail-box when she came in.

All her arrangements had been completed. Homer was
leaving for San Francisco tomorrow. The dear boy had
offered her three hundred dollars of his savings which she
could not dream of accepting. Socrates would be boarded
out with Mary. The piece of garden she had sold had been
marked off. Mr. Butler had proved quite nice. He was putting up a macrocarpa hedge. It was thick and grew quickly.
She had been able to cut the jobbing gardener down to half
a day a week. The problem now was to keep the weight of
her baggage down to the allowance. It seemed very little.
The grocer had weighed her portmanteau twice and each
time she had had to take something out and make substi-
tutes, but it was correct now.

The grandfather clock struck four. *Rome!* it reiterated.
Miss Allerton waited until the strokes died away. Then she
got up from her chair and turned on the light. She put the
magic tickets in their yellow and green folders on the desk.
The calendar said March 24. On the thirtieth she left.
Hardly a week now.

She went into the kitchen to fetch the tea-trolley left ready
by Mary. When the water had boiled she wheeled the trolley
out to the sitting-room. Socrates followed her in and out.
She gave him the biscuit due on this occasion.

"Two weeks from today you will be having your biscuit
in Mary's kitchen, and I shall be having tea on the Piazza
Colonna in front of Marcus Aurelius's column," said Miss
Allerton. "There are moments when I would like to call you
Cæsar."

CHAPTER II

I

"VIA APPIA," said the young hostess, pointing through the small window of the airliner. "We are now descending to Ciampino Airport. Please put on your belts."

Miss Allerton looked through the window. In the afternoon sun she saw the narrow straight strip, some cypresses, scattered roofs, and then as the plane wheeled, some white buildings that looked like factories or tenements. It was not at all Rome as she had imagined it. Ten minutes later, in the Customs room, she knew by the babel of Italian voices, by the inspectors and porters, that she was in Italy. It had been like going through a door in the clouds. She was tired, bewildered but proud of herself. She had not been sick, she had enjoyed her food. She had not had to take a sleeping-pill. Vaguely she knew that she had been in and out of Portugal and Spain, where some passengers had left the plane and others had come in. And here she was with her feet on Italian soil at last. She would have liked to get down on her knees and kiss it, but there was not any soil, it was all concrete.

In a few minutes she was conducted to a bus. There must have been a film star on board, such photoflashing, such bouquets, such a whirl of exuberant men round a small ginger-haired girl with an automatic smile heavily outlined in lipstick. She went off in a procession of private cars. The other passengers piled into the bus. They left the airport and started down a straight wide road, the sinking sun on their left. The landscape was flat, treeless and not at all romantic. Here and there gaunt new buildings, like concrete packing-cases, towered to the sky. She knew they were dwellings by the coloured washing hanging out. Then, suddenly, on her left she saw something that made her heart jump, a fragment of ancient Rome, the Rome of the Cæsars, standing there, solitary, silhouetted against the afternoon light in the flat landscape. She knew what it was at once. The series of arches in a level line, like a brown comb, were the ruins of an aqueduct. They stood there, gaunt, impressive, their purpose long gone, the first visible page in the great book of Roman history. Her heart beat faster.

They were drawing near a suburb. Huge blocks of buildings, ugly concrete dovecotes for human pigeons. Then came an old section, colour-washed in faded ochre and venetian red, and trams, buses, people, shops, stalls, swift glimpses of a piazza, a fountain and, lastly, a solid dark brick wall, with bastions and towers, through an opening in which the bus squeezed itself in a din of traffic. Someone said "Porta San-something." She could not catch the name. A few moments later she had a staggering glimpse of a great façade, with white statues of saints along the high skyline. It was not St. Peter's. "San Giovanni in Laterano," a voice said. It meant something to her then. It was one of the great basilicas to which the Pope used to ride in procession from St. Peter's across Rome, once a year, mounted on a white palfrey.

It all became confusing now. Great unpainted palaces, gates, church belfries with open arches and bells visible, high brick walls with heliotrope flowers cascading down them, whirlpools of traffic, sound of rushing water, long wide avenues crowded with traffic, lined overhead with lights, Roman policemen with white helmets and armlets, a pandemonium of buses, cars, people, lights, nothing that Julius Cæsar or St. Paul could ever have known, all conglomerated in the dusk as the airport bus whirled them onwards to their destination.

II

The Pensione Gigli was on the fourth floor of a great block of yellow-washed nineteenth-century buildings that stood high on the Via di Porta Pinciana. The upper storeys overlooked the tufted pines of Rome's great park, the Villa Borghese. When Miss Allerton arrived at the pension she was conducted to her room by a smiling landlady whose unintelligible English soon broke down, but she spoke good French. Miss Allerton checked her. "*Per favore, signora, parli Italiano. Io parlo un poco. Desidero imparare sua bellissima lingua,*" she said.

She carefully pronounced all the syllables. She felt like a gramophone disc, but it worked. Signora Gigli became quite effusive in delight and talked Italian at once, but at a quite incomprehensible speed. She rushed across the dim bedroom, opened a window and threw back the long shutters that gave on to a small balcony. "*Bella vista!*" she said, stepping back for her guest.

Miss Allerton went forward. It was indeed a beautiful view. It was so beautiful that for a few moments she could find no words and soon her sight was dimmed by the silly tears in her eyes. The sun had set beyond the pinewoods crowning the Janiculum hill across the Tiber valley. The calm upper sky was lemon and gold, the lower blood-red. "Dyed with the blood of the martyrs," she recalled. And there, beyond the valley, its vast dome and cross floating above the mauve dusk enveloping the city, sharply silhouetted against the bright gold of evening, rose St. Peter's. Between that vista and the foreground of the green Villa Borghese with its black umbrella pines, the Rome of myriad churches, domes, *campanili*, towers and palaces gleamed ethereally in the fading light. The upper air was filled with a shrill twittering and Miss Allerton saw that this noise came from the rapid criss-crossing of flocks of small birds, Roman swallows, in their vesper flight.

"*Eccola!* Villa Medici," said Signora Gigli, pointing to twin towers rising from a vast villa across the wooded park. "*L'Academia Francese.*"

Yes, she knew from *Walks in Rome* that it was the French

Academy in Rome, where the pupils studied who had won the coveted *Prix de Rome*. She knew also that it was where Velasquez had lived during his visit to paint his marvellous portrait *Pope Innocent X*; where Galileo had been interned during his trial by the Inquisition. She knew so much, she felt so much at this moment, that words forsook her and all she could say in response to Signora Gigli was *Si! Si!* And when the Signora left her alone, she continued to stand there, her heart full of inexpressible joy and sadness. She was overwhelmed by a melancholia of beauty evoked by the stupendous panorama fading in the evening light of Rome.

When the last colour had died and the evening star sparkled, she went indoors, closing the french window. There were three letters awaiting her on the dressing-table. One of them she opened at once before unpacking. It was from Anne in Beirut. To her great joy she read that she would come to Rome on the sixth of April. "I will be able to stay with you for some time. I am not returning here. I have not been altogether happy here, but more of that later. Reserve me a room, with you if possible, or at an inexpensive hotel nearby."

"Not altogether happy." What could have happened? Anne had seemed so cheerful in her former letters, enjoying the Lebanon scene, happy in her work. It was a shock to learn she had given up her post, though it was delightful to know that she would have her niece with her. But the letter worried her.

The room was small but cheerful, with a *cinquecento*-style canopied bed that made her think of a painting by Carpaccio in the "The Legend of St. Ursula", where the young princess slept with her crown at the foot. After a time a brass gong reverberated through the apartment. She went forth to her first Roman meal.

III

In the four days before Anne was due, Miss Allerton lost not a moment. She rose at seven, she set forth at half-past eight, Baedeker, camera, pocket dictionary, sketchbook and sunglasses in hand. She primed herself by reading the apposite history the night before. She contrived to be home at six each evening to enjoy the panorama of the sunset over the Villa Borghese.

She was pleased with her Italian. She chatted with everybody. Busy Romans helped her up and down in the buses; she knew at which end one went in and came out, and could give the correct money for the fare. But by the fourth day she found herself exhausted in two ways. She was emotionally exhausted. She lived in such a state of exaltation evoked by one discovery after another, of a picture, a column, a fountain, a temple, a vista, that her brain began to ache. Something else ached also. She learned that one of the most important things for sightseeing in Rome was feet. She had been shocked to see a German woman changing her socks while sitting on the altar steps of a side chapel in Santa Maria Maggiore, but she later thought how sensible the woman was. Her own feet were quite swollen.

She had given a day to exploring the Forum and the Palatine, lovely with its spring flowers. She had visited the museum and gallery on the Capitol. She had stood under the vast dome in St. Peter's, and peered down into the crypt at Canova's statue of the Pope kneeling in prayer. She had climbed to the highest tier of the Colosseum, determinedly shaking off the guides and the picture-postcard sellers. She began to wonder what she most liked in Rome, the equestrian statue of Marcus Aurelius proudly seated on his horse on the Capitol, Trajan's Column high in the brilliant sky, the Swiss Guards in their vivid orange and blue billowy breeches and large black berets, the view over Rome from the high balustrade of the Pincio gardens, the exquisite children playing amid the marble statues along the avenue of chestnuts behind the Villa Medici, the sun-bathed steps soaring up from the Piazza di Spagna, with its fountain and glowing flower stalls under bright umbrellas, the cafés with their awnings drawn against the sun, the blaze of flowerpots with geraniums, azaleas and roses along the Attic terraces of houses—wherever she stood, wherever she looked, the wonder of this timeless city, so modern, so old, so noisy, so quiet, so splendid, so squalid, filled her mind and eyes and caught at her heart.

On the fifth morning she had breakfast in bed and stayed in and wrote letters until lunch, which she took in the pension. After that she had a siesta. She wanted to be fresh for Anne, who was due that afternoon on the plane from Athens. She had been lucky in obtaining a room for her next to hers.

About four o'clock she heard some street musicians below her window. She went out on to the balcony. They were playing what looked like bagpipes and flutes. The music was thin and plaintive. The players wore shepherds' costumes, cross-gartered. One of them stopped playing and raised a conical black felt hat in salute on seeing her. She went indoors for a moment, found her purse, and threw them a note. What a sensation they would have created in Library Avenue, she thought. As she watched them she heard a voice behind her. She turned quickly. Anne stood there, a maid carrying her bag.

"Anne, darling!" she cried, going towards her.

Anne's arms went around her as she kissed her aunt. "All roads lead to Rome!" she cried, laughing.

"Are you tired, darling?"

"A little," replied Anne, removing her hat. "I'll soon recover."

"Some tea?"

"That's a good idea," she said and went towards the balcony. "What a view! However did you find this place?"

"Miss Allport was here last summer. You've a room next door."

She turned to the maid, "*Porti il bagaglio nella camera accanto e per favore mi porti due tazze di té,*" she said slowly.

"My! your Italian's wonderful!" exclaimed Anne, as the maid disappeared.

"You don't know how I've worked at it. Now sit down and tell me all about yourself," said Miss Allerton.

IV

They had been two days in Rome before Anne came out with her story. Miss Allerton felt instinctively that something had happened to make her niece "not altogether happy", but wisely she waited for her to open the subject. A constraint in manner, an intermittent pensiveness, betokened something unspoken. Then one morning Anne told her.

They were sitting in the garden of a little café terrace almost in front of the Villa Medici. Rome lay in the valley before them, clear in the morning sunshine. Immediately beneath clustered the antiquated houses and studios of the Via Margutta, the artists' quarter, their tumbling storeys opening on to the steep hillside covered with shrubs and vines. The café garden, hot in the sun, was ablaze with crimson and white azaleas. They drank their coffee in a little alcove aromatic with orange blossom.

"I suppose you've been wondering why I've left the University," asked Anne, playing with a coffee-spoon.

"Yes, you said in your letter you were not altogether happy. I can see there's something. You didn't like your post?" asked Miss Allerton.

"Oh, yes, I liked it immensely. Everybody was delightful, and I loved Beirut. It's most interesting and the setting's beautiful. I would have stayed there but——"

She hesitated, sat back in her chair and had a wistful, nervous smile as she turned to her aunt.

"I got engaged and broke it off," she said briefly.

Miss Allerton looked at her niece whose young beautiful face had an uncharacteristic solemnity. She had always been a girl of infectious gaiety and openness.

"There was nothing wrong with him, very nice really, a Virginia graduate who taught classical history. Brains, good-looking, twenty-eight. Very nice really, very alive and kind, and good company. We began to notice each other about a year ago. Last Christmas during a trip to Jerusalem—it was all very wonderful and went to our heads a little, the crowds, the processions, the midnight service in the Church of the Holy Sepulchre—we got engaged. When we were back in Beirut I began to have doubts."

She paused and looked across the terrace towards the wooded Janiculum that rose to the horizon.

"But you liked him?" asked Miss Allerton. "What was his name?"

"Paris Longstreet. It suited him; he was rather Greek in features, a straight nose coming in a line down from the forehead, his head covered with short fair curls, like the Praxiteles Apollo. He joked about his name, said mine ought to be Helen, and we'd be a real Trojan pair. Auntie, why do we call our boys after Greek heroes? Paris, Priam, Homer my brother, Hector, that red-haired boy in the drugstore—and even our cat, Socrates?"

"The reason is that we owe it all to the Greek War of Independence and Byron's death at Missolonghi," said Miss Allerton. "It started a classical revival in the States. That's how we got our columns in Library Avenue, I expect. Do you remember the Whaler's Church that summer we went to Sag Harbor? A real Greek temple of Corinthian columns, volutes, friezes. The Greek fever spread all over the country. Our young men wanted to go and fight with Byron, children were christened Homer, Ulysses—like President Grant—Paris, Hector. Well—your Paris Longstreet, tell me about him. You liked him?" asked Miss Allerton.

"I liked him a lot, but I found I didn't really love him. When I told him so he said it would come, he'd make it come. But I knew it wouldn't. You see, once you've been really in love and known the real thing, it's not the same. It can't ever be the same!"

There was a ring of conviction in her voice that made her aunt look sharply at her.

"You've been in love with someone else?" she asked, and then, reproving herself for her question, added, "Anne darling, you don't have to tell me anything unless you wish to."

Anne made no reply. Miss Allerton, glancing covertly at her, saw that her niece was on the verge of tears. So the poor child had had an unhappy love affair before she met Paris. If so, then it must have been in Germany, she surmised. How carefully Anne had kept her secret. Until now there had never been a sign.

"When I broke off with Paris," said Anne, after a pause, "he was very sweet about it. He couldn't quite believe it. I felt I just couldn't go on living in Beirut after that, so I resigned. Oh, Auntie, why is life so difficult!" she cried. "Look at this beautiful world and—and——"

She opened her reticule, took out her powder-case and dabbed her face.

"I've never understood why myself," said Miss Allerton quietly, fearing an emotional hiatus. "Life's specially difficult for women. Fate's put us on a raft, and we never know when to jump to the next."

"Were you ever tempted to jump?" asked Anne, smiling now.

"Once. Sometimes I think I should have done it. It might have been all right, or I might have been shipwrecked. But the strange thing about shipwrecked sailors is that they always go to sea again! Will you have another coffee?" asked Miss Allerton abruptly, fearing she was getting into deep waters.

"No, thank you, Auntie."

Miss Allerton looked at her watch. "It's nearly noon. We might walk along to the Pincio; I love the view, and then go down for lunch to a delightful little outside place on the corner of the Piazza del Popolo that I found the other day."

They rose, paid the bill, and walked away along the level terrace embowered in ilex trees. Miss Allerton was not going to press her niece. Perhaps one day she would get another instalment. Who was the other young man, and why hadn't it ended happily? Anne was now twenty-six. In four more years she would reach what she called "The Great Divide".

v

The next morning they visited the Fontana di Trevi and threw in their coins to ensure a return to Rome. Then they went towards the busy Via del Tritone. Miss Allerton suddenly stopped in front of a poster on a wall.

"There's one habit very irritating in Rome," she said, scanning a poster with a list of operas. "They won't advertise in the papers in advance! You never know what's going on, and you only find out after it's over. I've missed a performance of *Butterfly*, and last Sunday a Rubinstein recital. Now, what have we got here? *Don Pasquale*. It's one I've never heard. On Saturday, at the Opera House. Let's go, Anne. I'll treat you!"

Anne made no reply, she was reading another bill. Miss Allerton read the prices of the stalls. The figures had an alarming number of noughts, 5,000 lire. About eight dollars. An awful lot for Italy, she thought, but you paid at least ten dollars anywhere in America. And as Homer had once observed when she complained, "There are guys who think nothing of paying a hundred dollars for a prize-fight."

"You'd like to go, dear?" asked Miss Allerton, her niece not having answered her question. "It should be very fine. Hilde Gueden, she's very good. I once heard her in San Francisco."

Anne turned her head abruptly. "Yes—yes, it would be very nice, Auntie," she said absently.

"Then I'll get tickets," said Miss Allerton, walking on. She'd go without that handbag she'd seen. Presently she halted and looked at her niece anxiously. "Anne dear, are you all right? You're frightfully pale."

"I do feel a bit funny. It's very warm this morning, isn't it?"

"Yes, a touch of *scirocco*. Let's go into a café and sit down a bit."

They found a café and entered. Anne fought to control herself. She was not all right. She was all wrong in a world that had suddenly turned upside-down. While her aunt had been reading the opera poster she had been reading another one advertising the concerts at the *Argentina*. Next Sunday afternoon there was a performance by the Rome Philharmonic Orchestra. It was playing the *Merano Symphony*. The guest-conductor was Sir Aubrey Wellington.

Sunday afternoon. She would have to go. It would be simply impossible for her to stay away. Somehow she must go, alone. How could she get away from Aunt Grace?

VI

On Friday afternoon she slipped away, went to the *Argentina* and bought a ticket. She had thought of a plan. A California University friend, Millicent Brand, was studying singing in Rome. She would not ask her to go, but she would serve her purpose. She detested being deceitful, but she was desperate.

"Auntie, do you mind if I leave you on Sunday afternoon to go to a concert with a friend?" asked Anne at dinner that night.

"Of course not, my dear. You musn't feel that you're in any way tied to me," said Miss Allerton agreeably. "I quite expect that after *Don Pasquale* I shall have had as much music as I need."

It was that easy. She felt she was making a good fight to preserve a calm façade ever since she had been shaken by the poster. It would be a form of crucifixion to go to the concert, to see him conduct, to hear the *Merano Symphony*, her symphony, but it was impossible to stay away. The only man in the world she loved would be there before her eyes for more than an hour. She knew every bar of the symphony. She had played it again and again on her gramophone, evoking its composer.

VII

Sunday came. They spent the morning at the Baths of Caracalla.

"I wonder on which arch Shelley wrote *Prometheus Unbound*?" said Miss Allerton, surveying the massive masonry that towered up under the blue sky. "He used to climb up there in order to be undisturbed while he wrote."

The scaffolding for the open-air operas in summer was being erected. It looked like an iron spider's web.

"I'm sorry I shan't be here then, but one can't have everything. I'll be at the summer musical festival in Florence, and that's something!" said Miss Allerton. "Michelangelo's masterpieces on one side of the Arno and Verdi's and Puccini's on the other. What a land!"

She was doing most of the talking, she realised. Anne was obsessed by something. Paris Longstreet in Beirut, or the other unknown? There was something, she was sure of it. One day perhaps Anne would tell her. Meanwhile, being a tactful woman, she pretended not to notice anything.

VIII

There was not a seat vacant in the *Argentina* auditorium late on Sunday afternoon. The boxes were filled and every stall. All the subscribers had taken up their seats, many people were turned away. Anne, in the middle of the stalls, realised that she had been lucky to get a seat. She was in the presence of very serious musicians, she felt. The annotated programme contained a portrait of Sir Aubrey Wellington,

and of the solo violinist. The programme consisted of the
Mozart *Divertimento*, the Brahms *Violin Concerto*, the Bela
Bartók *Sonata No. 2*, and the *Merano Symphony*. This last
concluded the second half of the programme.

The auditorium hummed with conversation and the tun-
ing up of the orchestra. There was a solid mass of people on
the tiers rising to the organ at the back of the platform. As
the lights over the boxes lowered a hush fell. A tall slim
figure, in black morning coat and striped trousers, came
briskly in from the wing. There was a burst of applause. It
was Sir Aubrey Wellington. He went straight to the conductor's desk, bowed to the audience, turned and picked up
a baton. His right arm rose, paused, then came down on the
beat. The opening passage of the Mozart *Divertimento* pervaded the hushed auditorium.

Anne sat with eyes closed for a few moments. She had last
seen him standing and waving in the rain as the train drew
out of the station on a March morning two years ago. She
remembered also how she had first seen him in Munich when
he had conducted Mozart's *Die Entführung aus dem Serail*.
Nothing of her recollection of him had been dimmed. She
knew, as she had never doubted since those days in Munich
and Merano, that the man whose personality and genius had
first captured her heart still held it. The silence she had
imposed on herself through two years, the futile adventure
with Paris, had been in vain.

She opened her eyes and listened. The sensitive control,
the reserve of power, the musicianship held her as it held
orchestra and audience. When the piece ended and the
applause filled the auditorium, she sat quite still, entranced.

The conductor left the platform briefly. He returned,
following the violin soloist, a pale middle-aged man, exiled
from Poland. He bowed gravely and waited for his cue
during the opening bars of the *Concerto* until a beckoning of
the conductor's hand brought him in. It was a concerto in
which Brahms opposed the violin to the orchestra, but the

soloist was equal to the challenge. His *adagio* and *finale* were finely controlled. He won an ovation at the close.

At the interval Anne went out into the long vestibule. It was crowded. Every nationality seemed to be there, talking in Italian, French, English, German and Spanish. In one corner the *maestro* of the Accademia di Santa Cecilia held court. Anne recognised him. She had been introduced to him by her friend Millicent Brand when she had called for her one day at the Academy. Here they were, all the musical enthusiasts in Rome, part of that international world through which Aubrey Wellington moved with acclaim. She felt a little possessive and proud. How astonished he would be if he knew she was in the audience!

She went outside to get some fresh air, her head swam a little. Across the road, in a sunken space, walled in, were the ruins of four Republican temples, around which the city buses revolved in this modern day. The ruins went back to three centuries before Christ, their brown brick foundations now lit by the electric arc-lights, their tranquillity in the pool of Time shattered by the noise of motor buses filled with Romans. That was part of the wonder of this city, the juxtaposition of ancient and modern, the dead and the living.

She returned to the auditorium. The lights were still on over the boxes, the babel of voices rose in the Italian love of *chiacchiera*. A debate went on in her own mind. Should she go round and see him afterwards in the artists' room? Would he remember her? The question seemed fantastic, but it arose. He had not answered her final letter from Paris on the eve of her sailing for America. She had not written again, he had not written. But something in her life which she had thought might fade into just an episode had not faded. It was vividly alive, dominating her.

She would go round. She had to go round. He could not fail to be polite, to make a pretence of pleasure even if he did not feel it.

The lights lowered again. He came on to the platform, acknowledged the warm applause, took up his baton. The second half of the programme opened with the Bela Bartók *Sonata*. When it had ended there was a brief pause. The conductor returned to the platform, to begin the *Merano Symphony*, its first performance in Rome.

Anne knew every note of it. She knew the reason for every note. She saw the little town with the snow-capped mountains, she heard the running of the turbulent stream over its stony bed; there was the idyll of the mountain walk; yes, even the chalet with *Zimmer zu vermieten* which had started the impulse to send her the telegram. What glorious music, what genius to catch and transform the scene from sight to sound, missing no nuance of its enchantment! She sat, eyes half-closed, and let the music flow over her. His voice sounded again in the darkened room above the river.

The end of the symphony, a novelty to its hearers, brought conductor and orchestra a fervid ovation. Wellington returned four times to the platform before the audience had expressed its full enthusiasm. Then the orchestra left the stage and the stalls began to empty. Wedged in a queue, Anne contrived at last to reach the circular passage. Even now she hesitated, then, resolute again, asked an attendant for the way to the artists' room. She stumbled through the dark disorder in the wings and found the room. It was filled with people, the musical enthusiasts, the worshippers of celebrity, the social hostesses intent on securing the lion. Anne waited in the background, but at last a way opened for her. His recognition was instantaneous and eager.

"Anne!" he exclaimed, taking her hand. "It isn't possible! What are you doing in Rome?"

"I've come to join my aunt."

"Where are you staying?"

"In a little pension on the Via di Porta Pinciana."

"Wait a while. I must get rid of these people. You must dine with me. Thank God, I'm free tonight!"

She stood aside and let the "fans" attack again. It was twenty minutes before the last was disposed of. He took up his coat and hat.

"I've a car waiting. Come along. I'm at the Grand Hotel," he said, leading her towards the exit.

"My aunt will wonder where I am," said Anne.

"Your aunt? Oh yes, well, ask her to come along. No, Anne, put her off somehow. Telephone from the hotel. I must talk to you. In Rome of all places! And I thought you were far away in California."

"I haven't been in California for more than a year. I've been in Beirut. I've just come from there. It was by accident that I found you were conducting here," explained Anne.

They reached his car. When the chauffeur had shut the door his hand sought hers and held it.

"My darling Anne—you haven't changed in any way, except for the green hat with the cock's feather! How wonderful to see you again! You heard the *Merano Symphony*. You like it?"

"I'm terribly, terribly proud of it, Aubrey—even if I had only a little to do with it," replied Anne, her face radiant.

"You had everything to do with it. You created it," he said earnestly, his hand tightening over hers.

IX

On Tuesday Anne felt that she must tell her aunt. Her absences were being noticed.

"I've someone I want you to meet at lunch today," said Anne, going into her aunt's room.

"You don't have to tell me, I've seen it in your face for the last twenty-four hours. You've made it up. Paris Longstreet is here?"

"No—it's not Paris. Have you heard of Sir Aubrey Wellington?"

"The conductor? Of course I have. It's one of the reasons

I'm going to the *Maggio Musicale* at Florence next month. He's conducting twice—Strauss's *Der Rosenkavalier* and the *Merano Symphony*. He's wonderful. I saw in him San Francisco three years ago. But why do you ask?"

"He's here in Rome and we're invited to lunch with him today. I met him in Munich two years ago at Professor Salzer's."

"Anne, how wonderful! I'm thrilled."

"I've something more to tell you. We are engaged and going to be married as soon as possible, here in Rome," said Anne, desperately plunging now she had started the great revelation.

Miss Allerton, in bed, with a breakfast tray on her knees, put down her tea-cup with a great effort at steadiness.

"Sir Aubrey Wellington—the conductor? You're going to marry him? But Anne, he's an elderly man, old enough to be your father!" she exclaimed.

"And young enough to be my husband," retorted Anne. "Oh, Auntie, congratulate me, we're madly in love."

"Madly is the word."

"Darling Auntie, don't be stuffy!" pleaded Anne, leaning over and kissing her brow.

"I'm not stuffy, I'm staggered!"

"You'll recover when you meet Aubrey. You'll come?"

"Nothing will keep me away, my child. Why, it's one of the wonders of Rome," affirmed Miss Allerton, twinkling.

x

Now that it had to be arranged, it had to be arranged quickly. There would be a civil marriage at the Municipio, after the banns had been proclaimed for two weeks. They must be resident in Rome for these weeks. There were birth certificates and other papers to be produced. Wellington had been lent a Florentine villa for the Florence music festival by an Italian friend going to America. There they would spend their honeymoon while he fulfilled his engagements. Miss Allerton would stay in a pension on the Arno.

For two weeks Anne and Aubrey, sometimes accompanied by Miss Allerton, went sightseeing. They had glorious excursions in the Campagna, to hilly Frascati and Tivoli in the warm spring sunshine. At last their wedding day arrived.

It was a bright April morning, Rome looked her loveliest with her flashing fountains, flower-stalls, domes, towers and obelisks. They were married very simply in the *Sala dei Matrimoni* in the long portico of the Palazzo Conservatori, part of the municipal buildings that lined one side of the piazza on the top of the Capitol, the very seat of ancient Rome, once the site of the Temple of Jove. Outside in the vivid sunlight rose the bronze statue of the Emperor Aurelius, seated on his charger, hand imperiously extended towards the city below. A long flight of steps, flanked at the summit by marble statues of Castor and Pollux, led up to the magnificent piazza designed by Michelangelo. Surely there could be no more venerable setting for a marriage than this very altar of Rome's long history?

In the little tapestried room two large gilt chairs upholstered in crimson damask were placed for the chief witnesses. Flowers stood on the flat desk of the Mayor, who officiated. He was a resplendent figure with a broad silk sash in the Italian colours sweeping from one shoulder across his chest.

There were four couples to be married that morning. Aubrey and Anne came first. They stood between the two throne-like chairs, occupied by the British and American Consuls, who attended as witnesses. The Mayor delivered a little homily, cautionary and kindly, addressing the bridal couple, after the simple ceremonial that made them man and wife. There followed the signing and witnessing of the register. The bridegroom received a little book recapitulating the obligations of marriage. There were congratulations and much handshaking. In fifteen minutes it was all over. They gave place to a frightened peasant lad and his quite fearless young bride, buxom and smiling. A Press photographer caught them outside. Two days later they were in the *Daily Telegraph*. There was an announcement of their marriage in *The Times*. These, seen in Ligurio, when the papers arrived from London, caused a sensation in the English colony. Aubrey had kept their marriage very quiet. Not even Miss Pollitt knew until it was over. Mrs. Gavin was stunned and indignant. "The very idea! At his age, over sixty if he's a day, marrying a mere girl!" she exclaimed as she looked at the photograph.

She was sitting on the front at the Café Valentino. The Reverend Tobias Smollett smiled at her and said in his sweetest manner, "Now, now, Mrs. Gavin, don't be intolerant! I believe Joseph was a man of considerable years when he married Mary. They always make him look old on the Christmas cards. Let's wish them a long and happy life."

"And thank heaven we've got a young pretty face joining the colony!" exclaimed Lady Crossley. "We want some new blood."

CHAPTER III

I

THEIR three weeks' honeymoon was spent at the Villa Luccini at Ponte Arco, on a foothill looking westwards down the valley of the Arno. The river shone like a mirror as it wound towards Florence. From the wide terrace, with an ilex-flanked fountain at one end and a long balustrade from which a flight of steps descended to a flower-filled parterre and a small open casino, they had a view of Florence, the great dome of the Duomo, the Bapistery, Giotto's slender campanile, and the fortress-tower of the Palazzo Vecchio. To the left, beyond the arcaded bridge crossing the Arno, rose the sprawling Pitti Palace, backed by the terraces and woods of the Boboli Gardens.

The Villa Luccini was vast, a converted monastery with a fifteenth-century cloister and a pozzo down which its bronze bucket had not descended for a century or more. The interior walls of the open cloister were covered with frescoes faintly discernible after four centuries. The flagged floor had been worn by the passage of monks' feet. Only part of the villa-monastery was used. There was a huge refectory, impossible to heat in winter. It had a stage and proscenium built at one end.

"They must have had a theatre here!" exclaimed Anne as they stepped into the vast room with its long embrasured windows and high-raftered ceiling.

"Yes, before my friend bought it some years ago. It had belonged to an old boy called Crackenthorpe," said Aubrey. "He'd quite a history. He came here when young with a wild Russian girl. They spent money like water putting on operas and plays. Then one day she ran off with his Austrian factotum. He shut down the place and went round the world. On his return he became a miserly hermit for about twenty years. One day he fell ill and they took him to the convent-hospital of the Blue Sisters at Fiesole. There he fell in love with one of the nurses, a nun. She fled the convent and married him. They settled in Ligurio and he died two years ago, at ninety-two."

II

It took half an hour to reach Florence. They went in most mornings to shop, to drink coffee at Doney's and meet the Festival artists. The city was crammed. Aubrey conducted in the new auditorium and in the open-air theatre in the Boboli Gardens.

Miss Allerton in her pension on the Lungarno felt she was in heaven. She had worked her way conscientiously through the galleries. She began to patter about the Primitives, the Tuscan School, *chiaroscuro*, the "tactile" quality of the Fra Lippis in the Uffizi Gallery.

"Tactile?" asked Aubrey, smiling. "You've picked that up from Berenson, haven't you?"

"Why, yes!" replied Miss Allerton, a little shyly. "I think it's very expressive, don't you?"

"Most, and most appropriate, considering its origin."

"Appropriate?" asked Miss Allerton, puzzled.

"The great art critic lives in a villa called *I Tatti*," replied Aubrey mischievously.

They had a lot of fun together. It was often near midnight when in the warm starlit night he motored her back to Florence, sparkling in the valley. She had accepted an invitation to Ligurio after her visit to Venice.

One day walking on the terrace she had noticed a marble fountain with an inscription in English. "To Contessa Luccini, in gratitude. John Pears, David Woodburn, Piers Leigh." She asked Aubrey about it.

"It's a present from three English officers to our host's

wife. She's a very gallant Dutchwoman. She sat it out here all through the last war. She worked with the Partigiani, and hid three escaped English officers for a year or more, about 1944. The poor lads got very bored cooped up here. They were fond of music, so she used to take them down to the performances at the Festival, on the condition that they never opened their mouths. On one occasion they sat cheek by jowl with a German general. After the war they came back with their wives and gave her that fountain."

III

When the Festival ended Miss Allerton departed by bus over the Apennines for Bologna and Venice. Aubrey and Anne left for Ligurio by car. They stayed a night at Rapallo and the next day took the Via Aurelia through Genoa, along the Ligurian Riviera. In the early afternoon they drew near to Ligurio. The tortuous road rounding precipitous promontories, threading tunnels with blinding vistas, coasted along bays washed by a scintillating azure sea. They passed an island, tortoise-like, inshore. "They say St. Martin of Tours, the fellow who shared his cloak with a beggar, once took refuge there," said Aubrey, pointing to it.

Another great headland came into view. They climbed, rounded it and suddenly saw spread below them a long crescent bay, closed in by another great headland. At the top of the descent Aubrey stopped the car.

"Come along, I want to show you something," he said, taking his wife's hand and leading her across the road to a jutting rock high above the green-blue sea.

"Oh, how exquisite!" exclaimed Anne, as they stood in the hot sun, a golden crescent of sand, dotted with coloured umbrellas like a border of anemones, stretching before them. A town and its villas covered the valley and the foothills ringed by mountains. A thin pier put out a finger on the azure sea. The red and slate-grey roofs, the pink and white villas, the terrace gardens with orange and cypress trees, shimmered in the afternoon heat.

"There's Ligurio—your home," said Aubrey.

She made no reply except by her hand, which tightened in his. They looked at it while he pointed out various places, and then regained their car. Five minutes later they had taken the long straight road through the town with its orange-tree borders and palm trees, turned off from the sea-vistas, passed under a railway bridge and began the rise from the town to the Villa Tiberio.

Their coming had been awaited, and at the entrance, as they passed the gate, a surprise befell them. They were suddenly covered with a deluge of rose leaves.

"*Ben venuto! Ben venuto!*" cried a treble voice, followed by a peal of young laughter. A basket had been emptied over them from above. The next moment a figure had slipped down and a brown-legged boy in blue shorts ran excitedly in front of the car.

"Adelio, you young devil!" cried Aubrey at the wheel, shaking off the rose leaves.

The hall door was wide open. Young Adelio's cries had warned them all. As they got out of the car Miss Porritt appeared, excitedly smiling. Behind her in the dim marble hall the household was gathered: Giovanni and his wife, the cook; Maria, the parlourmaid; Francesco, the gardener, and his wife; and a youth, Bernardino, Giovanni's nephew. It was a royal homecoming.

CHAPTER IV

WITHIN a week it was as if she had always been there. Anne knew the shops in the narrow arched-over Via Umberto, the curving front with its cafés and promenade; the Café Valentino, where the English congregated in the morning; the newsagent's where they bought their London papers; the women's hairdresser, whose window, as you sat having a "perm", looked out on to the flowerbeds and palm trees of the Municipal piazza; the octagonal English Library, open twice a week; the tennis-courts, the bridge club, where Mrs. Gavin was the dragon, and the English church where, on a Sunday morning, the Reverend Tobias Smollett, white-haired, silvery-voiced, read the lessons but never preached. Aubrey had told her how, after his return from Merano, the Reverend Tobias had read *The Song of Solomon*. "The dear old man gave me a bit of a shock. It sounded to me like a *Liebestraum* solo and I wondered for a moment if he had heard anything."

Inside the villa Anne arranged flowers in the cool, shaded rooms. She had been a little apprehensive of Miss Porritt, whose domain it had been, but she received from her nothing but a motherly and tactful supervision. Lady Crossley had called, and the Contessa Verdecampo di Saluzzo, Mrs. Maysmith and Mrs. Callender had left cards. Then one morning at the Café Valentino, Mrs. Gavin had crossed to their table, saying, "Sir Aubrey, please introduce me to your pretty wife!" Later, outside, she turned indignantly on Mrs. Huddelstone. "What fool said she was only twenty? She's a well-disguised forty, if she's a day! But most agreeable."

There was one room in the Villa Tiberio that Anne treated with a certain reverence. If Aubrey was at work in it she kept away. It was the study, with his piano and big flat-topped desk with its signed portraits of Beecham, Furtwangler and Toscanini. Here the *Merano Symphony* had been born. One morning he had placed on the bureau in her lovely first-floor boudoir, with a loggia overlooking the town and bay, a volume bound in green leather. It was the manuscript of the symphony. Across the top sheet he had written: "To Anne, the only begetter."

They breakfasted on the pergola most mornings. Miss Porritt usually joined them. One morning, having gone to talk to the cook, she returned with a small green book. "Giovanni's just sent your suit to the cleaners. He found this in one of the pockets," she said, and gave it to him with a smile. He looked at the booklet. *Città di Roma. Stato Civile*, he read on the cover. It was the book of their marriage lines. He had completely forgotten it. He opened the slim book and began to read the Regulations tabulated inside. Presently he burst into laughter, so heartily that Anne, arranging flowers in the study, came on to the pergola.

"Anne, come here!" he called. "I've something to read to you. These are our marriage lines. When you married me in Rome you didn't know what you'd let yourself in for. Listen to this!"

She sat down on the swing lounge beside him as he read.

"*Article 131.* The husband is head of the family. The wife takes his status, his name, and is obliged to accompany him wherever he finds it necessary to live."

"I've no objection to that," commented Anne.

"You wait! *Article 132.* The husband must protect his wife keep her near him, and supply all the necessities of life"— he read and raising his voice—"in proportion to their means. The wife must contribute to the maintenance of her husband should his means be insufficient."

Aubrey handed her the book. "Now, my girl, look what you've done for yourself! What a clause for a lazy husband! Trust these Italians to look after themselves."

Anne laughed with him. "I think I'll have a second marriage—Church of England next time," she said, examining the book.

"I'm sure the Reverend Tobias would be delighted to oblige. And have you noticed the spaces reserved for the registration of children?"

She looked at the pages. There were twelve divisions.

"That's the Italian idea of a proper family," said Aubrey.

"I don't think we're likely to run out of space," commented Anne, laughing.

At that moment the sound of someone singing came up from the garden. It was a youth's voice, emotional, accompanied by the clip-clip of shears.

L'incanto d'una rosa, profumata, deliziosa, sei per me, mogliettina! sang the young voice below.

They listened. "It's Bernardino," said Aubrey.

"It's lovely. What does it mean?"

"'You are for me the loveliness of a delicious, scented rose, my little wife.' It's a bit flowery, but it expresses all I feel, *mogliettina*," said Aubrey Wellington, his hand covering hers.